To Kathy, Mary Beth & Joanne
from Nana   Feb. 5/1964

FORKED LIGHTNING

FORKED LIGHTNING

The Story of General Philip H. Sheridan

WRITTEN AND ILLUSTRATED BY

ALBERT ORBAAN

Hawthorn Books, Inc.   *Publishers*

New York and London

FIRST PRINTING

H-3735

PROLOGUE

"A steed as black as the steeds of night
Was seen to pass, as with eagle flight
As if he knew the terrible need;
He stretched away with his utmost speed
Hills rose and fell but his heart was gay
With Sheridan fifteen miles away."

—From "Sheridan's Ride"
by James Buchanan Read

In the dawn, at dusk, in sun ray and moonbeam and in the dark of night, the hoofs of the big black horse churned the earth where the powder smoke was the thickest and bullet whine and shell bang the loudest.

Sometimes the blue-uniformed men saw the horse clearly, pawing the ground nearby, at other times only dimly, a streak in the distance or a shadow in the battle fog. Whenever they saw the horse they would cheer and cheer again, and the flame that burned in the man astride the horse would stir them like an electric current. He would shout back, sometimes grinning, and wave the crumpled hat, and the men knew that everything would turn out all right for most of them because all that could be done would be done. That was the way it always was when "Little Phil" Sheridan on his big black charger, Rienzi, was watching over them.

CONTENTS

1. Wild Animal Trainer   9
2. Irish Fury   23
3. Wild Horse Land   33
4. First Command   43
5. Cavalry Raid   56
6. Victory!   66
7. Warhorse   74
8. Dread Field   88
9. River of Death   98
10. The Incredible Assault   104
11. Squadrons Charge!   117
12. "We Sent Them Whirling . . ."   132
13. Forward Everything!   143
14. "The Damndest Twist"   151
15. Galloping Nemesis   165
16. "Eyes Right"   175
    Further Reading   183
    Index   185

CHAPTER 1

WILD ANIMAL TRAINER

Little Phil was a trifle jittery when he entered the "circus ring" to fulfill his role as "Herr Dresbach, noted Prussian animal trainer."

Young Sheridan, then ten years old, knew that an ordeal of somewhat explosive possibilities confronted him. He had plenty of guts, however, in spite of his small size, and was determined not to fail his audience as the star performer in the "greatest vaudeville and circus show of all time."

The show was being held in an abandoned tobacco barn on the outskirts of Somerset, Ohio. A somewhat uncomfortable summery warmness pervaded the old barn, coupled with a lingering and pungent aroma of tobacco. At that time the circus was the main playtime enterprise of Henry Greiner, Phil, and a group of about eight other boys, their ages ranging from eight to eleven years.

On this day there was a larger audience than usual, consisting of some twenty boys and girls, all under twelve, and a few adults. This may have been because advance billing had been given to a "wild animal act" featuring Herr Dresbach.

There was nothing inside the barn to support the bombastic claims sprawled on a big piece of cardboard outside the door. There were just some hard wooden benches and boxes for the audience, partially surrounding a ring of cleared earth. Over the ring, fastened to a beam, was a rope with a loop in it. In the cleared area were an empty barrel, two boxes connected by a long pole and a rather ramshackle wooden cage with a hook-latch door.

The first performances—balancing acts on the barrel and the pole, a wrestling match and some cavorting on the rope—drew applause from the youngsters in the audience but left the few adults in a state of boredom close to sleep.

Spectator interest perked up when a rather large spotted dog and a big black tomcat were led into the ring on leashes by two boys. They were followed by Phil, barefooted, in rumpled trousers, a red sash across his chest, a switch in his hand.

Philip's appearance was anything but dramatic. He

was never impressive physically and he knew it. His arms were exceptionally long, his legs short, and the back of his head had a large bump on it. He had had to fight again and again over such insulting names as "baboon" or "monkey." Now his ear could detect some titters amid the clapping of the audience. He smiled not at all.

Without further ceremony the act got underway. Dresbach, the dog, and the cat entered the cage in that order. The act was timed so that every participant entered separately. Then the door was closed and hooked fast.

For half a minute there was uneasy peace in the cage. Then what was bound to occur happened. The dog made for the cat and a whirlwind running fight ensued with Little Phil plying his switch frantically, but to no avail.

There was loud applause which included shouts of "Keep on going, Phil!" "Give it to them, we're behind you, Phil!"

This was small consolation for Herr Dresbach.

Resigned to inevitable defeat and with no escape route available, the fearless trainer did the next best thing; he yelled for help. Greiner opened the door and the trio came out moving fast. The boy, badly scratched, halted his flight almost immediately, but the "wild animals" headed full speed for fields and trees beyond the barn door.

The exact date of this performance has been lost to history but is believed to have been in 1841. The man,

The trio came out moving fast.

who would fight Indians in the West and win world-wide fame in one of the bloodiest civil wars in history, always remembered it. He would say jokingly that it proved that he "had been in show business before turning to soldiering."

Philip spent virtually all of his early youth in Somerset, the son of poor but industrious Irish Catholic immigrants, John and Mary Sheridan. But Philip was not born there. There is a mystery to this day about his birthplace, although the date is known, March 6, 1831. Sheridan himself was an uncertain witness. On army documents, acceptances of promotions which required that he name his birthplace, he often named Somerset, sometimes Albany, sometimes Massachusetts. But no record of his birth can be found in Albany, Boston or Somerset.

His parents were married in County Cavan, Ireland, and lived and worked as tenant farmers on the estate of Cherrymount. All that is known of their forebears is that Philip's father claimed descent from the Irish kings. In 1830 John's uncle, Thomas Gaynor of Albany, New York, persuaded John and Mary to sell their leasehold in Ireland and invest their money in an ocean passage to America.

They landed at Boston and proceeded to Albany. Here John soon became aware that Gaynor's somewhat rosy statements about that city's opportunities for work were fanciful to say the least. He moved his family to Somerset, Perry County, Ohio, and found employment in the great road-building activity west of the Alleghenies. Many Catholics, particularly Irish immigrants, settled along the Cumberland Road and its tributary turnpikes and canals as transportation improved and wilderness areas became open to settlement and civilization.

In his personal memoirs, published in 1888, Sheridan declares that before leaving Ireland his parents had two children and "on the 6th of March, 1831, the year after their arrival in this country, I was born in Albany, N.Y., the third child in a family which eventually increased to six—four boys and two girls."

The Sheridan's six children were born in the following order: Patrick H. (born in Ireland), Phil, Michael V., John, Mary and Rosa. Sheridan's mother, whose maiden name was Mary Minor and who was born in 1801 in Ireland, had given birth to another daughter, but this baby died during the sea passage to America.

Very little is recorded about Patrick, Mary and Rosa. Both John and Michael eventually served honorably in the Union Army in the Civil War. Sheridan mentions them in his memoirs but does not refer in any descriptive form to the others. None, except Phil, achieved any great distinction. Although he was fond of all his brothers and sisters, Phil's favorites evidently were John and Michael.

The town of Somerset was built on a high ridge between the Hocking and the Muskingum Rivers. In spite of the fact that it was a small place with only some twelve hundred persons living in it, Phil and his companions never found life dull. Big Conestoga wagons heading west passed through regularly and the young boys of the town would eagerly listen as the wagoners told tales of the hazards and adventures they encountered on their dangerous routes across the country. Forests and fields were not far away and wide open to any kind of engrossing activity.

All the boys living in the western, or Hocking, side of the town, were known as "Pig Foots" and all those living on the eastern, or Muskingum, side were "Turkey Foots."

Sheridan and his brothers were automatically "Pig Foots." Clashes between members of the two factions were almost incessant, with Little Phil always in the thick of it whenever some real or imagined injury· was being righted. The fights were not serious affairs, usually being limited to fisticuffs and various types of wrestling, yells and kicks. No serious injuries ever occurred, even when sticks or stones were brought into play.

In his youth Phil had a highly inflammable temperament, not an unusual Irish trait. He was always ready to fight at the drop of a hat, regardless of the size of his opponent. In later years he learned to curb his violent temper, after being impressed with the importance of self-control when his fighting ardor got him into serious trouble at West Point.

The bump on the back of his head was not the only unusual physical feature of Phil Sheridan. According to one description given by a long-time friend, "One could tell from his Mongol-type eyes in a moment whether he was fiercely angry or only indignant; whether he was serious, sad or humorous, without noticing another feature of his face. I never saw eyes which showed so many shades of feeling as those of Phil Sheridan."

There was little question that young Phil had a natural leaning toward soldiering. Frank Burr and Richard Hinton wrote in their biography of Sheridan, "Phil Sheridan was, from his earliest boyhood, a lover of soldiers. His eyes danced and his heart beat whenever there was a drill of the village militia company. Every summer he would get a dozen of his schoolmates and persuade them that it was the best fun in the world to play soldier. His friend, Sam Cassell, would let him have a sword of the sharpest and brightest tin and, of course, Phil was always captain. But there would always be some mutinous boy who wanted to be captain, too, and Sheridan's company usually broke up in confusion."

Young Phil was by no means an outstanding scholar, however, and did not care much for school. The teachers of that time in towns like Somerset were not a kindly lot. They were poorly paid, used the rod freely for the slightest misdemeanor, and cared little for their students or their profession. This did not tend to foster great respect for them among the pupils.

In his memoirs, Sheridan has left us a rather humorous description of what school life was like in those days.

"When I was old enough I was sent to the village school which was taught by an old-time Irish 'master,'" he wrote. "He was one of those itinerant dominies of the early frontier named McNanly. He held that to spare the rod was to spoil the child. If unable to detect the real culprit when any offense had been committed, he would consistently apply the switch to the whole school, without discrimination."

McNanly was a tall, bony man. He particularly liked staying at the Sheridan house because he had known Phil's parents in Ireland. He also had a rather kindly feeling toward the little Irish boy, but he had another favorite, a boy named Home.

One day Sheridan and Home had it out in the schoolyard. Phil unleashed a haymaker with his right fist and blood flowed from Home's nose. Home promptly ran howling to McNanly inside the school. The teacher, infuriated by the damage inflicted on one of his favorite pupils, grabbed a stick and went out to administer justice. Phil was sitting on a rail fence, seemingly unconcerned, blowing on his knuckles, his eyes on the school door. When the teacher stormed out, Phil whistled, scrambled off the fence and took to his heels, the teacher in panting pursuit, hickory stick twirling.

The closest sanctuary for Phil was the shop of Sam Cassell, the tinsmith. Sam, who was seventy years old and still climbed the courthouse steeple to repair the brass globe on the spire, was Phil's best friend among the adults of Somerset. It was Sam who had fashioned Phil's first sword, and a warm comradeship had developed between the two.

The chase led up the middle of the main street, and everybody rushed out to see it, shouting and laughing. Uttering terrible threats, the long-legged teacher began to gain on the boy. Phil made a beeline for the tinsmith's shop and dashed into it, gasping for breath.

"Hide me, Sam, teacher's after me bad!" Phil begged his friend.

There was not a second to lose. Sam was at work on a big copper kettle. Quick as a flash he clapped the kettle over the boy, and, when the teacher arrived, Sam was quietly hammering away at a rivet, within two inches of the fugitive's head.

"Where's that dratted Sheridan boy who ran in here?" the teacher asked, his face purple.

"What boy?" Cassell asked with an innocent look on his face.

The teacher cast a suspicious eye around the shop but did not spy Phil and resumed his search outside. Almost immediately Phil emerged from his hideout and, having regained some of his wind, raced back to the school. He was sitting at his desk, slanting eyes fixed on the ceiling, when the teacher came puffing into the room. McNanly was so astounded that he did nothing about it, and class was called to order.

Eventually McNanly decided to leave Somerset and headed for the howling wilderness west of the Mississippi. History does not record what happened to the unhappy schoolmaster.

He was succeeded by a Mr. Thorne. He proved to be just as harsh a disciplinarian as McNanly. Thorne was a Virginian with some of the haughty mannerisms for which people from that state were known in those days.

18

It is believed the characteristics of this teacher instilled in young Phil his lifelong scorn for Southerners who thought they were "gentlemen" and better than others because of the place of their birth.

When Phil reached the age of fourteen he went to work as an apprentice and later as clerk in two local stores, first with John Talbot and then with *Fink & Dittoe's Drygoods Store.* He proved a good worker and learned a lot about bookkeeping. This knowledge would stand him in good stead in his military career, for his excellent handling of military paper work was noticed by important superiors.

In spite of his clerical work, Phil dreamed of someday becoming a soldier. From the very first he had loved horses and had no fear of them. As often as he could he would climb onto the half-broken stage horses and ride them bareback. The thought that he might combine his desire to be around horses with a military career spurred him on in his effort to gain his goal.

Although his school days were over, Phil avidly read all kinds of books, notably those dealing with military history.

Recalling the days at *Fink & Dittoe's,* he wrote in his memoirs:

"The Mexican War, then going on, furnished, of course, a never-ending theme for controversy. Although I was too young to enter the military service when volunteers were mustering in our section, yet the stirring events of the times so much impressed me that my sole wish was to become a soldier and my highest aspiration to go to West Point as a Cadet from my Congressional district."

At first Phil's chances of ever getting to West Point seemed remote. Then one day he learned that the original appointee to West Point from his district had failed to pass the examinations. Phil promptly wrote to his representative in Congress, the Hon. Thomas Ritchie, and asked for the appointment. Ritchie responded by enclosing a warrant for Phil for the class of 1848.

Phil was overjoyed, but there were issues that still had to be settled. Besides the fact that Phil's education had been a meager one, his father had some misgivings about sending his son to a predominantly Episcopalian institution. The matter was solemnly placed before Fathers Dominic Young and Joshua Young, the two Dominicans who had supervised Phil's religious instruction. Father Joshua reportedly opposed Phil's going to West Point on the grounds he might lose his faith.

Apparently the matter was the subject of considerable debate in the Sheridan family. It is not mentioned in Phil's memoirs; perhaps he did not like to recall it. It is believed the boy's father realized that his misgivings were not fully justified, that his son was set on it, and in further discussions secured the Dominicans' approval. In any case, it was formally decided that Phil should go, much to his joy.

"At once I set about preparing for the examination which precedes admission to the Military Academy," Phil wrote in his memoirs. "I studied zealously under the direction of my new teacher, Mr. William Clark; my old teachers, McNanly and Thorne, having disappeared from Somerset to seek occupation elsewhere."

On a sunny day of early summer, 1848, Phil stood in the dusty main street of Somerset awaiting the stagecoach which would take him to Zanesville, Ohio, on the first leg of his journey to West Point.

All the other members of the Sheridan family were present. Boyhood chums and adult friends of Phil had joined them to say farewell, including old Sam Cassell, the Dominican Fathers, and his oldest boyhood pal, Henry Greiner.

Phil was neatly attired in a brown suit and held himself erect and proud. In spite of his seventeen years, he still looked young and puny. The boys of the town, including the biggest, had long ago ceased insulting Phil in any way. By this time it was known that he could thrash any boy in town.

Down the road came the swaying stagecoach at a fast clip. John gave his son a warm hug and a pat on the shoulders as the stage came to a creaking halt, horses snorting.

"Fear God, but fear no man, Phil. You'll make out fine, me boy, we know you will," John said.

His mother, tearful but smiling, embraced and kissed

her boy and bade him godspeed. Then Phil entered the coach. The driver cracked his whip, and the coach jounced away toward Zanesville.

The carefree days of boyhood in familiar surroundings were over for Philip Sheridan. Ahead of the border-town boy was a vast, mysterious world strange to him. In it he would face dangers which would tax his bravery and resourcefulness to the utmost. The Indian war-whoop would ring in his ears, and he would play a stellar role in one of the bloodiest wars of all times, the war with twenty-five hundred recorded engagements, the American Civil War. He would wield "forked lightning" against his enemies, the men in butternut and gray.

CHAPTER 2

IRISH FURY

The cadet-lieutenant was the very embodiment of military spit and polish as he strode unsmiling toward the two Ohio boys standing on the wharf of West Point Military Academy.

The two newly-arrived rookies were Phil Sheridan and David Stanley, another West Point applicant from Ohio whom Phil had met on his journey. David was the same age as Phil, although a chunkier and somewhat taller lad.

Both suddenly felt terribly alone as they gazed at the paddle steamer *New World* knifing away down the Hudson River, at the forbidding cliffs of West Point, and the approaching officer. Both felt like Robinson Crusoes suddenly deposited on some strange island where such as they were extremely unwelcome.

Neither had ever seen anything quite like the personage approaching them, except in pictures in books. The officer walked ramrod straight, his eyes fixed in a cold stare on the new arrivals in their rumpled clothes.

The brass buttons of his gray full-dress coat glistened, his gloves and trousers were impeccably white, the trousers pressed to boardlike stiffness. He wore a black, saucer-like forage cap, slanting downward toward a patent leather visor. His mustache was neatly trimmed and the gold stripes of a cadet-lieutenant graced each of his shoulders.

"You are candidates?" he snapped.

"Yep, I'm Phil Sheridan and this is David Stanley," Phil said with a half-grin.

"When you answer me, say 'sir' in all cases," the officer replied frowning. "You're speaking to an upperclassman. I asked you a question. I don't care about your names. Again, are you candidates and answer quickly."

"Yes, sir," the overawed boys answered promptly in chorus.

"Very well, follow me and I'll find you some cots and some food and step lively," the officer said harshly.

Picking up their bags, the two boys followed the cadet up the hill. At the top, on the steps and porch of the boxlike Rider's Hotel, stood some ninety boys also in civilian clothes.

"Those creatures over there may be your classmates—

if you are lucky and pass your examinations," the officer said. "They're from practically every state in the Union. You'll stay with them in the hotel. Tomorrow at eight you will be rounded up and marched to the adjutant. Then they'll check you at the hospital. After that the examiners will see what you know."

The West Point "welcome"—if it could be called that—chilled the enthusiasm with which Phil had undertaken his journey. The trip from Somerset, although long and complex in those days, had all been a delightful experience for him.

From Zanesville he had taken passage on a barge on the Ohio and Erie canal to Cleveland, everywhere gazing on new sights and talking with all kinds of people. From Cleveland he had proceeded to Buffalo on a paddle steamer on which Stanley also was a passenger. At Buffalo he beheld his first locomotive and went by train to Albany to visit an uncle for a few days before continuing to West Point. Stanley, who had decided to go by canal boat to Albany, rejoined him there and both had then taken passage on the *New World*.

Phil and Stanley soon realized that the ship had truly brought them to a new world, its keynote unrelenting discipline and hard work. The years ahead at West Point would be crucial ones for Phil. His fiery temper would almost end his military career before it had begun. At the same time he would learn one of the most important lessons of his life—that hot anger can prove disastrous and must be controlled.

After a few days David and Phil passed their first

examinations—which in those days were really little more than a literacy test—and became members of the Cadet Corps as of July 1, 1848. The passing class consisted of sixty-five young men from all parts of the country. They included George Crook, who would become a noted Civil War and Indian fighter, and Henry Slocum, future Union corps commander in many big battles and campaigns. Slocum would turn out to be a very helpful friend to Phil during troubled days at West Point.

It proved hard for Phil, used to the easygoing ways of Somerset, to adjust to the caste system at the military academy. At that time West Point was dominated both professionally and socially by men from the southern states, most of whom considered themselves the elite. To them there was practically nothing lower in the social scale than an Irishman born of immigrant parents, who was Catholic and came from a northern state.

The "monkey suit" worn by cadets consisted of a stiff single-breasted gray coat with swallow tails, gray trousers with a black stripe at the sides, white gloves and a high-crowned black hat with an eight-inch plume and a leather cockade. No uniform could be found which could fit Phil perfectly. The sleeves always were just a little too short and the trousers too long. His hat, which had to be an outsize one, always seemed about to fall down to the tip of his long nose. As a military specimen he was definitely sub-par, outwardly at least.

Following his admission, Sheridan was broken in by "hazing." Although officially forbidden, upperclassmen, particularly in those days, plagued the newcomer "plebes" relentlessly with all kinds of hazing pranks. Plebes on sentry duty were frequently stripped of their uniforms and deprived of their muskets by "raiders" disguised in white sheets. Others were told to perform details which the upperclassmen had no right to order. On several occasions Phil was the victim of rather severe hazing but apparently managed to keep his temper in check.

Although he had passed the entry examinations, he knew that a much stiffer examination was impending in January, 1849. His knowledge of algebra and higher mathematics generally was still very unsatisfactory, his spelling nothing to brag about. He was lucky enough, however, to have Henry Slocum as roommate. Slocum had had an excellent education and proved a real friend in need.

"After taps—that is, when by Academy regulations, all lights were supposed to be extinguished and every-body in bed," Sheridan recalled, "Henry and I would hang a blanket over the one window of our room and continue our studies—he guiding me around scores of stumbling blocks in algebra and elucidating many knotty points in other branches of the course with which I was unfamiliar . . . on account of this help I went up before the Board with less uneasiness than otherwise would have been the case, and passed the examination fairly well."

Although Phil was only a plodding mediocrity in the classroom, he took to horse and saddle as if born to it and showed himself quick in grasping all types of cavalry and other field problems. This repeatedly drew favorable comment from his superiors. In other "field problems"—unofficial fist fights—he proved himself a very tough opponent who would brook no insult. Whatever laughter was brought forth among fellow classmen regarding his appearance was not heard when Phil was within earshot.

Everything appeared reasonably serene for Phil when he returned to West Point from his first furlough in Somerset in July and August of 1850. He had made some good friends at the academy, notably Slocum and George Crook, and during the ensuing twelve months pursued his studies with fairly satisfactory results. But the Irish temper was still there, and in September, 1851, Phil was involved in an incident with a haughty Virginian cadet sergeant which taught him a lesson he never forgot.

One afternoon Sheridan and other men were drilling under the cadet sergeant, William R. Terrill. Suddenly Terrill, whose tongue could be very cutting, told Sheridan he was incorrectly "dressed" (aligned) and to remedy this immediately.

"He said this in an improper tone," Sheridan claimed. "I believed I was properly dressed and fancied I had a grievance."

To Sheridan virtually anything Terrill did or said amounted to a grievance. The Virginian, to him, was a symbol of all the slights and social snubs he had endured at the hands of Southern "gentlemen."

Phil headed for Terrill with lowered bayonet.

In the brief ensuing argument, Phil became so enraged that he swung his musket and headed for Terrill with lowered bayonet, something no soldier should ever do, especially to a superior officer.

Fortunately Phil's better judgment caused him to halt before any "actual contact could take place." In that split second Sheridan saved himself and changed the course of his life. Although no bloodshed or real combat had occurred, he was in grave trouble. This was a breach of discipline which could not be overlooked, and Terrill would have to report it.

A few hours later, when the men were off duty, Phil went after Terrill with his fists outside one of the barracks. Terrill, bigger than Phil and in excellent condition, was just about to give the Irish gamecock a thorough lambasting when a West Point staff officer stopped the fight and asked both combatants to submit letters of explanation.

In following days the explanations given by both men were carefully considered by academy authorities. The upshot was that Phil was suspended for a year and only resumed his studies with the class of 1853, starting in the fall of 1852. The blow was a hard one, yet in many ways a just and mild punishment in view of the flagrant insubordination.

After he returned to West Point in August, 1852, he again became embroiled in various fights, but not in public, in off-duty hours and usually by mutual agreement. In some of these he got the worst of it and the sight of Phil being brought back to barracks with a bloody nose or black eye was not uncommon. Phil's various duels became almost a daily subject of conversation but brought him no official punishment.

When graduation time came in 1853 he was thirty-fourth among fifty-two in scholastic standing. At graduation he was within five demerits of expulsion, his many fist fights having come to the attention of the Academic Board. The story circulated later that Phil actually had exceeded the limit for demerits but the authorities felt he should be passed anyhow, that such an aggressive spirit would someday make him a useful officer.

At that time the top cadets were assigned to either the engineers, the cavalry or the artillery, which were considered the choicest branches of the service. It did not come as a surprise to Sheridan that he had been assigned to a branch which did not have as much prestige but was vital to winning battles—the infantry, known to GI's of today as "footsloggers."

The class of 1853 included a number of men who would make their mark in American military history. There was John Bell Hood, who would become a full general in the Confederate Army and would lead the Army of the Tennessee at Atlanta, Franklin and Nashville; Joshua Sill, who would become a Federal brigadier general and die in action leading his division in the battle of Stones River in which Sheridan participated; and John M. Schofield, who in the years after the Civil War would succeed Sheridan as commanding general of the United States Army.

It is noteworthy that one of the leading members of the West Point faculty at that time was a Virginian named Robert E. Lee. He would become supreme Confederate military commander in the Civil War. His path and that of Sheridan were destined to cross again as enemies.

Another remarkable man on the faculty was cavalry instructor George Thomas, also a Virginian. In years to come, Thomas, unlike most men of his state, would decide that it was his duty to fight for the Union. He would be one of its most famous commanders. Both he and Phil would be involved in notable battles and become good friends.

Commissioned a brevet second lieutenant, Sheridan received orders to join the 1st Regiment, U.S. Infantry, at Fort Duncan, Texas, after a leave of three months. Phil, pleased with the appointment since it meant adventure in Indian fighting territory, promptly returned to his hometown where the days passed pleasantly in the company of family and friends.

In September he again said good-bye to Somerset, heading for Newport Barracks, Kentucky, from which young officers were routed to new commands. Eight years would pass before he would see Somerset again, and then only briefly.

On March 10, 1854, Brevet Second Lieutenant Sheridan boarded a steamer heading south on the Ohio and Mississippi run. Real armed action was in the offing for the one-time tin sword soldier of Somerset.

CHAPTER **3**

WILD HORSE LAND

The wild horses, many-shaded, long manes and tails flying, would appear and disappear as if by magic before the spellbound eyes of the young officer in the dusty uniform. To Phil these first glimpses of the animals thundering untamed across plains and hills were among the most outstanding recollections of his long and at times very tedious trip to Fort Duncan.

The journey to the fort, on the Rio Grande, near the Mexican town of Piedras Negras, was far longer and more rugged than the jaunt from Somerset to West Point. After reaching New Orleans, he crossed the Gulf of Mexico by steamer to Indianola, Texas, and from there went by small schooner to Corpus Christi. This was the headquarters of Brigadier General Persifer F. Smith, commanding the Department of Texas.

Phil, who as a lad had proved himself a keen observer of people and localities, would have made an excellent newspaper reporter. In his well-written memoirs he has left us an engrossing account of his journey to the fort and subsequent adventures.

"A day or two after my arrival at Corpus Christi a train of Government wagons, loaded with supplies, started for Laredo, Texas, a small town on the Rio Grande below Fort Duncan. There being no other means of reaching my station I put my small personal possessions consisting of a trunk, mattress, two blankets and a pillow into one of the heavily loaded wagons and proceeded to enter it, sitting on the boxes or bags of coffee and sugar as I might choose."

The wagon train moved slowly into the wilderness, covering only a few miles on the first day. As dusk fell, camp was made at a spot where there was plenty of grass but little wood or water.

"There being no comfortable place to sleep in any of the wagons, filled as they were to the bows with army supplies, I spread my blankets on the ground between the wheels of one of them. I awoke in the morning feeling fresh and bright. . . ."

It took the lumbering train many days to reach Laredo, which is about 160 miles from Corpus Christi.

At Laredo Phil left this caravan for a six-mule wagon carrying various supplies to Fort Duncan.

Sheridan's lack of social graces and his unprepossessing physical appearance were a handicap, as far as human relations were concerned, almost from the very start of his tour of duty at Fort Duncan. Friction between himself and Lt. Col. Thompson Morris is glossed over in that part of his memoirs dealing with life at the fort, a lonely outpost consisting of some fifteen adobe buildings in a dreary plain. It is known from other sources that Phil and Morris disliked each other intensely from the very first.

The lesson learned at West Point stood Phil in good stead here, however. From the outset Morris made his dislike known in many irritating ways. As a brevet lieutenant Phil had to gulp down his anger and remain impassive, which he did.

Fortunately, Captain Eugene E. McLean, commander of "D" company to which Sheridan was assigned, was a different type of man and liked Phil in spite of his lack of social polish. Phil would never forget the kindness of McLean and his wife. In fact, it was their attitude that made things endurable for him. Time and again Mrs. McLean with smiles and tactful words would dispel Phil's gloomy spirits after some disagreeable session with Morris and prompt him to forget his reticent ways and be more friendly toward others.

However, Phil's greatest pleasure was riding in the surrounding country. He was always accompanied by a soldier named Frankman, "who was a fine sportsman and a butcher by trade."

There was plenty of wild life in Texas in those days

and Phil became an expert and ardent hunter under the guidance of Frankman who was a veteran in this field. Frankman did not have to teach Phil shooting, because Sheridan was already a fine marksman.

This hunting was actually done at Camp La Pena, some sixty miles from Fort Duncan, used principally as a scouting base to keep an eye on roving Lipan and Comanche Indians whose raids were troubling the area. Company "D," its commander, and another company had been shifted to this camp almost immediately after Phil's arrival. This was a fortuitous event, for it removed him from the immediate vicinity of Morris.

The fact that Sheridan, a commissioned officer, was often in the company of an enlisted man like Frankman was frowned upon by most of the officers, but Phil's democratic leanings and his liking for Frankman were not altered one whit as a result of this attitude. This was characteristic of the officer who in momentous campaigns would state repeatedly, "Put your faith in the common soldier and he will never fail you."

The camp at La Pena was on sandy ground "unpleasant for men and animals," and on Sheridan's advice, which found favor with Captain McLean, it was shifted to a place called La Pendencia, a few miles distant.

One bright morning on a scouting detail with Frankman, Phil made his first valuable contribution in the constant watch for suspicious Indian movements.

"We saw a column of smoke on the prairie," Sheridan recalled. "Supposing it arose from a camp of Mexican rancheros catching wild horses or cattle . . . which were very numerous in that area along the Nueces River, we thought we would join the party."

It was a good thing they did not. Proceeding along a creek, the two men found moccasin tracks and soon realized that Indians were involved and "all Indians in that country at that time were hostile." Both men swung their horses around and made "eager strides"—no doubt full gallop—for their own camp.

Sheridan immediately informed Captain E. M. van Buren of his discovery. The captain had just trotted in with some thirteen men of the Mounted Rifles in pursuit of a band of Comanches which had raided the vicinity of Fort Clark, another Texan military outpost.

Sheridan, Frankman, Van Buren, and his command, at a rapid trot, reached the point from which the smoke had arisen. There was no doubt that Indians had camped there and departed recently. Sheridan and Frankman returned to their own camp but Van Buren and his men pursued the Indians day and night in the direction of Corpus Christi. Finally, the Indians, angered and exhausted by this remorseless hunt, "halted on an open plain, unsaddled their horses, mounted bareback and offered battle."

The Mounted Rifles were heavily outnumbered, but on orders of their captain charged headlong at the hostiles. In the fray the courageous cavalry captain was mortally wounded by an arrow which entered his stomach just above his sword belt and came out through

Sheridan and Frankman returned to their camp.

the rear part of the belt. The Indian chief was killed and the Comanches fled. Van Buren was taken to Corpus Christi where he died a few days later, in terrible agony.

When the La Pendencia troopers were pulled back to Fort Duncan for winter quarters late in 1854, Phil was very resourceful in relation to his personal comfort. He built himself a solid hut of wooden poles and tarpaulin, thatched with prairie grass. It had no window, but sufficient air came in through various chinks in the walls and a small door could let in light when necessary. The floor was of dirt, "compactly tamped." The furniture was very primitive.

"A chair or two, with about the same number of camp stools, a cot, and a rickety old bureau that I obtained in some way or other. My washstand consisted of a board about three feet long, resting on legs formed by driving sticks into the ground until they held it at a proper height from the floor."

Most of the other officers contented themselves with remaining in tents during the winter and viewed Phil's "home building" as rather unmilitary. When winter winds began to howl they thought otherwise, and this did nothing to increase Phil's popularity at the mess table.

During the winter months of 1854 and 1855, Sheridan made his first acquaintance with a formidable drinking concoction, a fermented potion used as a medicine to prevent scurvy caused by insufficient vegetables. To drink it would test the fortitude of any man in any place. And Phil not only had to drink it again and again but had to gather the plants necessary for its production.

"To prevent scurvy we used the juice of the maguey plant, called pulque. To obtain a supply of this antiscorbutic I was often detailed to march the company out about forty miles and load up two or three wagons with pulque stalks."

In the fort the juice was extracted from the stalks in a rude press and put into bottles until it fermented. The odor of this liquid, when it had reached full bloom, was worse "than sulphurated hydrogen," Phil recalled with a grimace.

"At reveille every morning this fermented liquor was dealt out. . . . It was my duty, in the case of Company "D," to see that the men took it. I always began the duty by drinking a cup of the repulsive stuff myself . . . every man in the company then gulped down his share regardless of its vile taste."

The chances of gaining military distinction in combat were very slight at the fort and in its vicinity. The post was too strongly held for any mass attacks by the border tribes, the Comanche, the Lipan and the Apache.

One incident did occur which proved to be Phil's last brush with the Indians during the Fort Duncan assignment. A band of raiding Lipans pounced on a discharged drummer boy herding cattle within sight of the fort's flagstaff. Sheridan and men of the Mounted Rifles under a Captain J. G. Walker immediately pursued the raiders. They found the body of the boy riddled with arrows. He had not died easily, however. Next to him lay the body of a "fine looking Indian" whom he had obviously killed with his own hands before he was overwhelmed.

The cavalrymen pursed the Indians relentlessly but the latter crossed into Mexico. Once in Mexico they dared the company to fight them, but the pursuers knew they could not cross the border without causing serious international repercussions. It was a favorite Indian maneuver which inevitably left their opponents enraged and baffled.

Although Sheridan was genuinely interested in knowing more about Indian customs and characteristics, he could only obtain sketchy information in routine patrols and scouting missions. As a result he came to share the opinion of most white men that Indians were just "bloodthirsty savages." History has shown the gross error of this view and proven that the American Indian had fine qualities of courage and loyalty and was the victim of outrageous white repressive action, lacking any semblance of honor.

Late in 1854 Sheridan was promoted from Brevet Second Lieutenant to Second Lieutenant—a slight promotion—and received orders transferring him to the 4th Infantry. In the spring of 1855 he left Fort Duncan to take on his new assignment, after bidding a warm farewell to Captain McLean and his wife, Frankman and some other friends at the post.

Another journey—the longest of his youthful years—was underway for Phil. He had been assigned to Fort Reading in the Pacific Northwest. But first he had to report to the New York area to take charge of a number of recruits also headed for that zone.

In this region of mighty mountains, lakes, rivers and plains Phil would get his first taste of real combat in which he would actually command fighting men. His adventures would prove far more stirring than those at Fort Duncan.

CHAPTER 4

FIRST COMMAND

In May of 1855 Sheridan arrived at Bedloe's Island, in New York Harbor, where the Statue of Liberty now stands. The 300-odd recruits slated for shipment to the West were an unruly, disgruntled lot, dissatisfied with their food and shelter, on the verge of mutiny. Phil immediately proceeded to adjust matters, enforcing strict but just discipline and acting energetically to provide the men with better victuals, clothing, and shelter. In a few weeks he had restored order, his efforts on their behalf winning the respect if not the affection of all the men.

The entire contingent, jointly commanded by Sheridan and a Lieutenant Francis H. Bates of the 4th Infantry, embarked early in July, 1855. They reached Benicia Barracks, the Army's main depot north of San Francisco, late that month. The long voyage had been by ship except for an overland haul across Panama. The famous canal would only be built years later.

Shortly after his arrival at Benicia, Sheridan was ordered to catch up with an expedition under a Lieutenant R. S. Williamson, a topographical engineer. This expedition was making surveys to determine the possibility of building a railroad between the Sacramento Valley and the Columbia River region. This project had been given particular importance by the discovery of gold in Oregon territory.

The whole area was swarming with Indians, particularly irritated by the influx of prospectors whose mining operations were ruining their rivers and killing the fish on which they largely depended for food. The Pit Indians and other tribes in this area were starving.

Phil was pleased with the assignment. He had been ordered to take over command of forty dragoons, serving as mounted escort with the expedition. George Crook was also with the expedition, and there would be plenty of good stories to swap when they got together. And at last he would have a real command, forty full-fledged dragoons instead of his one-man force, Frankman, in Texas.

"Lieutenant Sheridan, you will proceed to Fort Reading, the base of operations of the expedition," the Benicia commander told Phil. "You can proceed alone

44

on horseback if you wish. The hostiles are north of the fort. But I would suggest that you join a wagon train we are sending to the fort within a few days. It is a long jaunt, 250 miles at least, I warn you."

"Thank you, sir, for the information," Phil replied. "I would like, however, to leave immediately with your permission if I can be supplied with a horse."

The commander considered the matter carefully and then said smiling:

"All right, Lieutenant, I can see you are determined to join your command posthaste and that's all to the good. You have my permission. The stable sergeant will give you a horse. Good-bye and best of luck."

Phil obtained his mount, a sturdy chestnut, and left alone that same day for the fort. He was suitably dressed and equipped for such a trip: large felt hat, blue woolen shirt and trousers, cavalry boots and spare socks and underwear, rifle, six-shooter and saber, field glasses, rolled-up cavalry overcoat, saddle bags containing food, blankets and some rough maps of the area.

His journey was uneventful, consisting mainly of hard, steady riding. Phil reached the fort in five days. Somewhat to his disappointment the commandant informed him that Williamson had left about a week previously and urged Phil to delay his departure until he could continue with suitable escort. Phil was eager to proceed, however, and persuaded the fort commander to give him an immediate escort. It was his first command in the field—two troopers and a corporal.

The four horsemen headed first eastward and then northward as shown on the map. At Fort Reading, Phil had been informed of the general route of the expedition, which was largely dismounted, and the trail was fairly easy to follow. All four maintained utmost vigilance because this was dangerous territory where belligerent Pit Indians were active.

Sheridan soon realized that they were following a double trail, that a band of Pit Indians was following the Williamson party. This sharpened Sheridan's natural alertness, and his reactions showed he was a born frontier fighter.

"We followed the trail of the Williamson party until about 4 o'clock in the afternoon when we heard the sound of voices and my corporal, thinking we were approaching the party, was so overjoyed in anticipation of this that he wanted to fire his musket. . . . This I prevented his doing. We continued cautiously and slowly. We had not gone far before I discovered that the noise came from a band of Pit River Indians who had struck the trail of the surveying expedition."

Dismounting, Sheridan carefully scanned the moccasin tracks and found that the Indians numbered about thirty and probably were on Williamson's trail with "evil intent." Phil and his men followed the trail but kept their distance from the Indians. At night they lit no fires and their supper consisted of "hard bread only." The next day the Indians, who were afoot, armed with bows and arrows, saw the small party of white men in the Hat Creek area.

Knowing that he must be near the Williamson party, Sheridan decided that he and his men would have to make a galloping dash for it. They put spurs to their mounts and headed at full gallop through a wide valley. The Indians did nothing. They knew that the soldiers could not cross Hat Creek, which had steep vertical sides, except at one point where there was a ford. The Indians were near the ford. But to the astonishment of the soldiers, instead of attacking, the Indians were making unmistakable gestures of friendship.

"We were obliged to halt and the Indians continued their demonstrations of friendship, some even getting into the stream to show that they were at the ford and that we should cross there."

Although he was justifiably wary, these demonstrations finally reassured Sheridan, and he and his command headed their horses for the ford and boldly crossed it with Indians shouting and waving on either side.

After they had crossed the creek and gained a bluff on the other side, they looked down into the valley of the Pit River and could plainly see the camp of the Williamson party.

"Its proximity was what had doubtless caused the Indians to be peaceable. Probably the only thing that saved us was that they were ignorant we were in their rear until we stumbled on them almost within sight of the larger party under Williamson."

That day, August 4, 1855, Sheridan entered the Williamson camp and was warmly welcomed by the commander and his officers. The following day the expedition moved eastward along the Pit River and then headed northward toward the Klamath Lakes.

The journey involved some hard riding and walking but proved extremely peaceful. In the Klamath Lakes area they met some six hundred half-starved Pit River Indians and provided them with food.

In the Three Sisters area the column split. Williamson, Sheridan and his dragoons and others headed for the coast and the Willamette River, while the infantry under another officer went to the Mt. Hood zone. In October both wings rejoined and camped opposite Fort Vancouver in a beautiful valley along the Columbia River.

There were a few peaceful days at the new encampment and then came trouble. Late that month the Yakima Indian War broke out. The Yakimas, whose territory lay to the east of Fort Vancouver, had killed their government agent and had repulsed a punitive army column seeking to avenge the killing. The Indians captured two mountain howitzers, but this did not mean very much since they did not know how to use such ordnance.

At the end of October, Phil was ordered to prepare his horsemen for action and join a second expedition against the Yakimas under command of Major Gabriel Rains of the 4th Infantry. The column was composed of Regular Army troops from the Vancouver area and a regiment of Oregon Mounted volunteers.

Sheridan was elated at the prospect of action, but he would return from the campaign anything but elated. In fact, the whole campaign would turn into something of a farce. The crafty Yakimas adopted effective will-o'-the-wisp tactics and in a general sense emerged victorious.

During the second day of the advance toward the Yakima Valley, Sheridan and his dragoons caught up with a small band of these Indians, scattered them, and seized most of their winter food supply. A few days later, riding in the van as scouts, they saw a cloud of dust on a plain between them and the main force. Sheridan feared that it was caused by Yakimas who had cut them off.

"There seemed no alternative left but to get back to our friends by charging through these Indians," Sheridan recalled.

Sabers and six-shooters drawn, shouting madly, the dragoons and their commander galloped toward the dust cloud. The group who had caused the cloud showed Phil and his men the rear ends of their horses. Both contingents thundered pell-mell into Rains' newly established encampment. Phil's "enemies" were not Indians but Oregon volunteers who had for a moment believed the dragoons were Indians. The incident caused a hearty laugh all around but did nothing to improve relations between volunteers and Regulars and caused Phil some embarrassment.

The following day at about 1 P.M. "we saw a large body of Indians on the opposite side of a river."

On orders from Rains, Sheridan and his horsemen plunged into the river. They had succeeded in getting across when the Yakimas rushed them yelling like fiends. Phil, cool and experienced by now, ordered his

Fort Vancouver
Columbia River
Portland
Mt. Hood
Willamette River
Three Sisters
Des Chutes River
Klamath Lakes
Klamath River
Lost River
Pit River
Fort Reading
Hat Creek
Lassen's Butte

men to dismount, kneel and open fire. The fire was heavy and threw the Indians into confusion, wounding some.

When Rains had brought the remainder of his force across, the Indians massed on a high crest and taunted the white soldiers.

"Most of them were naked, and as their persons were painted in gaudy colors and decorated with stripes of red flannel, red blankets and gay war bonnets, their appearance presented a scene of picturesque barbarism, fascinating but repulsive. They numbered about 600. . . . In addition to firing occasionally they called us all sorts of bad names, made indecent gestures and aggravated us."

Sheridan and other officers and troops moved against the ridge and the Indians withdrew. When the soldiers pulled back—their officers feeling that they were not strong enough to launch a major attack—the Indians again concentrated on the hill and hooted at them. This continued until nightfall when the Indians vanished.

This was a more or less typical incident in the campaign, which dragged on for weeks. Phil and his dragoons and other companions never really got to grips with the Indians, since the entire operation was hampered by Rains' indecision and delaying tactics.

After weathering fearful winter storms, the expedition headed back for the Vancouver region. Quarrels broke out between Rains and his officers—Sheridan excluded—and one of them preferred charges of incompetence against Rains. Nothing came of it, and Sheridan noted in his diary that the expedition was considered a "wretched failure."

In the spring of 1856, the Walla Walla, Spokane, Yakima, Umatilla, and Nez Perce Indians went on the warpath in Oregon and Washington, encouraged by the white man's poor showing in the Yakima campaign. In large numbers they virtually surrounded a key block-house on the shore of the Columbia River, just north of a river island named Bradfort, about fifty miles east of Vancouver. Many settlers fleeing from raiding Indians had sought refuge in the blockhouse.

Phil and his men were ordered to proceed upriver on the steamboat *Belle* to the relief of the blockhouse. A supporting column would advance overland. Phil's troops would be the spearhead. Until he was joined by the other column, he would be the top officer.

Late in March, Sheridan's force disembarked from the *Belle* on the north shore of the Columbia, about four miles from the blockhouse, along with a small cannon used mostly for saluting purposes for which Phil had obtained cannonballs. Then he sent the steam-boat back to Vancouver to bring up possible reinforce-ments but kept a rowboat with him.

His position was precarious, to say the least. He and his forty men were on a narrow neck of land, the Columbia River on their right. To their left was low water caused by overflow of the Columbia, then in heavy flood. The Indians, in considerable numbers, were on the north shore between them and the block-house. Without waiting for reinforcements, Phil, with characteristic daring, immediately started skirmishing with the Indians and they returned the fire. An Indian bullet almost got him.

"It grazed my nose and struck a soldier standing close to me in the neck, opening an artery and killing him instantly," Sheridan wrote.

The dragoons, who had no mounts with them in this operation, repelled several rushes by strong bands of Indians, in which a number of the soldiers were lightly wounded. Phil, supremely elated, his fighting spirit at top pitch, was everywhere in the front ranks. On his order the little cannon was brought up and fired repeatedly into the undergrowth in which the Indians were massed.

The fighting stopped at nightfall. Phil realized that there were too many Indians between him and the blockhouse on the north shore. Then he evolved a plan.

In the early morning hours of March 28 he and his men crossed the river to the south shore in two trips, the rowboat carrying twenty men each time. With them went the small cannon. Thus far the plan had gone smoothly. After climbing a hill on the south shore, Sheridan could see across Bradfort Island through his field glasses. The Indians, apparently unaware of his departure, were indulging in horse races and otherwise amusing themselves.

Then came a hitch in the plan, one that added to Phil's "terrible anxiety." It was found that the heavy rowboat could not be moved along the southern channel of the Columbia because rapids were too violent.

Phil called for ten volunteers to help him drag the

boat along the southern shore of the island where the water was somewhat shallower and calmer. Sheridan picked his volunteers, and the remaining thirty soldiers advanced toward the blockhouse along the mainland shore.

On the island, while working the rowboat through the eddying waters, the force came upon a camp of old squaws who had been left there for safety while the braves disported themselves on the north shore. Phil, with "unmistakable threats, made them not only keep quiet but also give us needed assistance in pulling vigorously on the towrope of our boat.

"They worked well under compulsion and manifested no disposition to strike for higher wages," he commented with rather heavy humor.

The rowboat was again brought to the south shore, and Sheridan landed on the north shore in the immediate vicinity of the blockhouse. Before the Indians, who numbered some four hundred of the Yakima and Cascade tribes, could take any counter-action, Sheridan was joined by the overland column. In a few hours the blockhouse was relieved and the Indians dispersed or captured.

This was Sheridan's last actual combat in the Northwest, although he remained there for some five more years. He and his dragoons were transferred and stationed for most of the time at Fort Yamhill, at the Grande Ronde reservation in Yamhill County, Oregon. Here Phil kept an eye on the Chinook Indians and even learned their language.

During these years, Sheridan and the other men in

such remote outposts, were kept informed of events elsewhere in the country. But all the information, contained mostly in newspapers, magazines and letters, came very late, carried the greatest distance by pony express.

When he received news that the guns had thundered against Fort Sumter and that the Civil War had started, it still came as no great surprise. The eventuality had been discussed in army circles for years.

As the Union Army grew, it needed competent officers. Sheridan, whose service record was excellent, and whose sympathies were certain, was promoted to captain. He was assigned to the 13th U.S. Infantry Regiment, at Jefferson Barracks, Missouri, near St. Louis, then commanded by a relatively unknown general named William Tecumseh Sherman.

On September 2, 1861, the man from Somerset, just turned thirty, a veteran Western campaigner, his face the color of mahogany, left Yamhill on horseback for Portland where a steamer awaited him. His journey would take him to New York and St. Louis, again via Panama.

In the East was a big black horse, taller than any Phil had ever ridden, with flashing eyes, veins rich with Morgan blood. They would meet within a year. The horse also was destined for fame, like Alexander's Bucephalus, Napoleon's Desirée and Wellington's Copenhagen. The stallion would be named Rienzi. No man would prove more faithful to Phil than this warhorse, two years old in that momentous year of 1861.

CHAPTER **5**

CAVALRY RAID

Whatever dreams Phil may have had that his transfer
from the West would immediately lead to exciting
combat went up in smoke late in 1861 and in the first
five months of 1862. In fact his duties often reminded
him of his bookkeeping and other tasks at *Fink &
Dittoe's* in Somerset—lots of paper work and handling
of supplies, day after day. However, Phil did perform
these with remarkable industry, honesty and intelligence, and his efficiency bolstered several important
Union operations.

The Confederate threat was particularly serious in
the important border states of Kentucky and Missouri,

which were in what was known as the western theatre of operations. Phil was headed for that area. These states—which President Lincoln rightly believed must be kept in the Union—were endangered by two main factors: the Confederate Army of the Tennessee under General Albert Sidney Johnston, and a struggle for supreme Union authority between Major General Don Carlos Buell and Henry "Old Brains" Halleck. Halleck soon won out. At this time Johnston was threatening to advance in Kentucky, a move which would endanger the Ohio River line and its busy cities. At the same time Southern forces under another commander, Sterling Price, were massing in southern Missouri and northern Arkansas for an offensive aimed at the recapture of St. Louis. Although the picture was not too rosy for the Union, there were two good factors: its armies in this western theatre were being reinforced daily at a rate which the Confederacy could not duplicate; gunboats and other ships were going into action in ever-increasing numbers, bringing strategically important waterways under Federal control.

Technically, Phil was a captain in the 13th Infantry, a new regiment created by Lincoln in the swift expansion of the Regular Army. This regiment nominally was commanded by Sherman but Sherman at this time actually led a division of the Army of the Tennessee commanded by Ulysses Grant.

Obeying his orders, Phil proceeded to St. Louis and late in November reported for duty to Halleck, then Commanding General of the Armies of the Tennessee, the Ohio and the Mississippi, his headquarters far from the camps of the 13th Infantry.

Halleck was a middle-aged man with popping eyes, lofty forehead and a hesitant manner, an intellectual rather than a practical soldier. He had translated and written a number of military textbooks, lectured on military and historical affairs at Harvard, and he held degrees in engineering, law, and military science. He just could not undertake swift maneuvers and favored cautious moves which drove such men as Grant and Sherman to the verge of distraction.

Phil was just the man Halleck needed at that moment: someone capable of straightening out the accounting mess left by "Old Brains'" predecessor, flamboyant Major General John C. Fremont.

Although annoyed by this desk appointment, Phil attacked with a will and, with the aid of some assistants, in two months had generally restored order out of chaos. He performed his tasks so well that Halleck marked him down as a very promising officer.

At the beginning of 1862, Phil was transferred to the staff of Major General Samuel R. Curtis, commanding the Army of the Southwest. This army was being prepared to push the Confederates out of southern Missouri and tackle Sterling Price once and for all. The 15,000-man army was then in camp at Rolla, southwest of St. Louis, and Phil was appointed chief commissary and quartermaster of this force.

The supply system of the army was in considerable disorder, and complex and nerve-wracking problems were shouldered by Phil during ensuing months. In addition to organizing a smooth flow of food and other supplies to moving forces, Phil had to cope with graft and intrigue among dishonest subordinates, of whom there were quite a few in this army. Road communications were poor; the country was rough and a large section of the population unfriendly toward the Union. Some regiments had perhaps fifty wagons while others had three or four, a glaring imbalance which Phil corrected with some difficulty.

On January 26, 1862, Curtis' force began its march from Rolla toward Springfield, southwestern Missouri, via Lebanon. Sheridan went with the army, and some of the difficult problems which he faced are cited in his memoirs:

"The roads were deep with mud and so badly cut up that the supply trains in moving labored under the most serious difficulties and were greatly bothered by swollen streams. Under these circumstances many delays occurred and when we arrived at Lebanon nearly all the supplies with which we had started had been consumed. The feeding of troops off the country had to start at that point."

The Federals entered Springfield unopposed after a Confederate withdrawal toward Pea Ridge, Arkansas. Phil remained in Springfield to toil further with army logistics. The campaign ended on March 6 when Curtis and his men scored a decisive victory at Pea Ridge. Sheridan contributed greatly to the victory by keeping supplies rolling smoothly through country unfriendly to the Union and scant in farm produce. But Phil would always fume about his service with this army. General Curtis was never very cordial toward him and, Phil felt, did not appreciate all his hard work as quartermaster.

When he returned to St. Louis, Halleck sent him on a roving commission to purchase horses. After the terrible battle of Shiloh Meeting House, near Pittsburg Landing, in northern Tennessee in April of that year, Phil was assigned to Halleck's staff.

"Old Brains" persisted in considering Phil just a very good staff officer. As a result, he was ordered to supervise the corduroying of swamp roads and to keep wagons and railroad trains moving. The wheels of destiny were spinning on his behalf, however. He would get the action he craved in a few weeks. Sheridan had acquired influential allies and had repeatedly pleaded for transfer to some combat command.

One of these backers was General Sherman. He recommended that Sheridan be given command of an Ohio Volunteer regiment, partly because Phil came from Ohio. In those times it was still up to the governor of each state to appoint such officers. The Ohio governor turned down Sherman's suggestion. Then Brigadier General Gordon Granger, who had just been promoted to this rank after serving as colonel commanding the 2nd Michigan Cavalry, took up Phil's cause.

He persuaded Governor Austin Blair of Michigan,

then at Pittsburg Landing visiting the Union forces, that Phil should be made a colonel and put in command of the 2nd Michigan. A young captain of the same regiment, Russell A. Alger, who would become Secretary of War in later years, seconded Granger's request. The Governor consented, and as of May 27, 1862, young Phil was designated a colonel in command of the 2nd, which comprised some four hundred sabers.

"It was the turning point in my career," Sheridan later told friends.

Phil was jubilant; "paper work" and the dull chores of the past were at an end. Now there would be adventure, dangerous riding and the chance to really distinguish himself as a combat soldier.

Phil had to move in a hurry. The very night of his appointment the 2nd Michigan and the 2nd Iowa Cavalry, some 827 men and officers, were going into action as a brigade under command of Colonel Washington Elliott. The brigade had been ordered to conduct a raid south of the Confederate base at Corinth and strike at Confederate General P. G. T. Beauregard's railway connections, particularly Booneville, Mississippi, twenty-two miles to the south. This town was astride the Mobile and Ohio Railway, main enemy supply line.

Bidding good-bye to various officer friends, Sheridan mounted his horse and pounded southward on a twenty mile ride into northeastern Mississippi.

"At about 8 o'clock that evening I made my appearance at the camp of the 2nd Michigan Cavalry, near Farmington, east of Corinth. The regiment was in a hubbub of excitement, making preparations for the raid. I had barely time to meet officers of my command and no opportunity at all to see the men, when the trumpet sounded to horse.

"Dressed in a coat and trousers of a captain of infantry, but recast as a colonel of cavalry by a pair of well-worn eagles that General Granger had kindly given to me, I hurriedly placed on my saddle a haversack, containing some coffee, sugar, bacon and hard bread . . . mounting my horse, I reported my regiment to the brigade commander as ready for duty."

Following a circuitous route, Elliott's brigade moved southward, meeting scattered Confederate resistance. The "rebs" were quickly dispersed or eluded. Booneville was occupied on May 29 and the cavalrymen burned twenty-six railway cars containing ten thousand muskets and pistols, three pieces of artillery, and a great quantity of clothing and ammunition supplies.

With part of the men of the 2nd Michigan, Phil galloped southward and destroyed stretches of track of the Mobile and Ohio Railway, Corinth's main link with the South. Confederate squadrons attacked Sheridan and his men while they were disrupting the railroad. Under Phil's alert command, these were repulsed by heavy fire from the Colt repeating rifles used by his cavalrymen.

Meantime, trains from Corinth began piling up at Booneville with wounded and convalescent soldiers of

Illinois

Ohio

Indiana

Missouri • St Louis

• Louisville
• Perryville

Kentucky

• Rolla
• Lebanon
• Springfield

Tennessee

• Pea Ridge

Pittsburgh Landing

Arkansas

• Corinth

• Booneville

Mississippi

Louisiana

Gulf of Mexico

"Old Brains" Halleck

Beauregard's forces. Corinth was being evacuated. Sheridan pulled back to Booneville, rejoining the rest of the brigade.

During this operation the 2nd Michigan captured some five hundred Confederate stragglers and convalescents. But it was too much of a problem to bring these prisoners along with them, and Phil turned them loose "after breaking up their guns."

The position of the raiding party now was a particularly dangerous one. It might be overwhelmed by some large enemy force moving out of Corinth. Without any delay the brigade headed back for Farmington, which it reached safely, completing a successful attack involving a ride of at least 180 miles.

The raid was actually the only serious blow struck in an effort to thwart Beauregard's masterful withdrawal from Corinth. It might have been less masterful if someone other than "Old Brains" Halleck had been on his trail. Halleck, moving with elephantine slowness, never came to grips with Beauregard. By May 30 Corinth had been emptied of troops, supplies, civilian population and railway locomotives and cars.

In early June, Phil led the 2nd Michigan in a strong reconnaissance in the wake of the retreating enemy. He reported from Baldwin, Mississippi, a town south of Booneville, that Beauregard was heading for Tupelo and applying "scorched earth" policy as he moved.

"The enemy drive away and carry off everything for miles around," Sheridan noted. "Many families, even those among the wealthiest, are destitute and starving. . . . Our cavalry passed many fine houses where women and children were crying for food."

Phil's coolness under fire, his excellent "feel" for cavalry action and his tireless energy had drawn favorable attention. After returning from this reconnaissance, he was put in command of the whole brigade on June 11. Elliott had been promoted to brigadier and designated Chief-of-Staff of the Army of Mississippi. Phil was still a captain, but moves were underway formally to promote him to brigadier and this rank would come soon.

The erstwhile army bookkeeper had done very well. In two weeks he had doubled the number of men under his direct command. Within three weeks the 800-odd cavalrymen would follow Phil into the smoke and flame of his first major battle—the battle of Booneville. It would occur just west of this town, the same one he had raided. The odds would be some 5,000 to 6,000 "rebs" against 827 Federals!

CHAPTER **6**

VICTORY!

During June, Phil worked hard to bring the brigade to higher combat efficiency. He managed to provide better food and shelter and dispelled several causes of irritation. It was in this period that he formulated his credo for the field, a sound one in any time or place and a key to Phil's success in military life.

"Men who march, scout and fight and suffer all the hardships that fall to the lot of soldiers in the field, in order to do vigorous work must have the best bodily sustenance and every comfort that can be provided. I knew from practical experience on the frontier that my efforts in this direction would not only be appreciated but requited by personal affection and gratitude; and, further, that such exertions would bring the best results to me.

"Whenever my authority would permit I saved my command from needless sacrifices and unnecessary toil; therefore when hard or daring work was to be done I expected the heartiest response and always got it. . . . Soldiers are averse to seeing their comrades killed without compensating results . . . they want some tangible indemnity for loss of life and victory is an offset the value of which is manifest."

Late in June, Sheridan was ordered to garrison Booneville, then in advance of the main Federal lines. Once there, Phil immediately started to learn everything he could about the terrain near the town, drawing fairly accurate maps for himself and his officers. He dispatched strong scouting patrols into the surrounding country and personally checked his camp picket lines day and night. He was preparing for a surprise.

Unlike most other commanders of that time who felt that cavalry should be used as cavalry and nothing else, Sheridan always considered horsemen nothing more than infantrymen "with four detachable legs." As a result, most of his men were dismounted and placed in a clever defense cordon at Booneville in forested areas, protected by rifle pits and felled lumber where necessary. His vigilance never ceased and paid off "handsomely," as he noted in his diary.

A big Confederate force, larger than he anticipated, was on the move from the southwest under General

James R. Chalmers to wipe out this irritating Federal outpost.

Early in the morning of July 1, 1862, one of Sheridan's pickets west of the town spotted the enemy. Skirmishing began almost immediately, and the dismounted Federals fell back to the main lines. They had barely done so when the Confederate horsemen hurled themselves against the main positions, on horseback and dismounted.

The Federals fortunately had greater firepower than the enemy. Each man was equipped with a Colt revolving rifle and a six-shooter, able to fire twelve rounds without reloading. The hurricane of bullets shattered the first Confederate onslaught, inflicting many casualties. But General Chalmers kept on attacking with everything he had. The Federals held their positions in hours of fighting, gunsmoke swirling through the thickets and fields, the screams of wounded men mingling with the almost constant rattle of musketry. By noon, however, Phil realized that only very bold action could save his command from being completely wiped out.

In addition to the frontal attacks from the west, Chalmers had now started a flanking move toward Sheridan's headquarters camp north of Booneville.

Setting spurs to his chestnut, Phil galloped to the positions held by the 2nd Michigan and reined up before Captain Alger, who was a man of exceptional daring and coolness.

"Captain Alger, take four saber companies immediately out of the line," he said. "You are to strike in the enemy's rear. A dangerous job, Captain, but it must be done."

Hurriedly, Phil explained his plan. Alger's companies—only ninety horsemen—would strike at the enemy's rear in a cavalry diversion, following a forested path north of the Blackland Road. The saber companies would be accompanied by a Missouri guide named Beene, who knew every nook and cranny of that vicinity.

"I expect you to attack them in the rear in about an hour," Phil said. "Simultaneously, I will launch an attack with all my forces. You are to charge in column right through whatever you come upon and report to me in front of Booneville, if it is at all possible for you to get there. When you attack, make as much noise as possible so that we will know you have gone into action."

The column was soon assembled and Phil watched it disappear among the trees, outwardly calm but inwardly "very anxious." He knew the whole thing was a desperate gamble, one which weakened his already small main force at the scene of the heaviest fighting.

As the designated hour drew to a close, the Federal position became increasingly grave, menaced by enemy flanking operations. Earlier in the day Phil had sent a message to the town of Rienzi, divisional headquarters, to hurry infantry reinforcements and artillery to Booneville, but nothing had come.

"All along our attenuated line the fighting was now sharp," Phil recalled. ". . . the enemy's firing indicated

VICTORY!

such numerical strength that fear of disaster to Alger increased my anxiety terribly as the time set for his cheering arrived and no sound of it was heard."

A minor but fortunate event now occurred. One of the most vivid descriptions of what befell at this time, in mid-afternoon, was penned by Frank Burr and Richard Hinton.

"True to his promise, when the hand pointed to the last moment of the hour, Sheridan prepared for the charge. Just as he moved out for the final stroke, a train of cars came down the railway and drew into Booneville, sounding its shrill whistle as a warning and a welcome to those in battle. The train was bringing forage for Sheridan's horses from Corinth. Everyone in the Union lines knew that Sheridan had sent for reinforcements and the arrival of the train thrilled the struggling soldiers with a new hope.

"They began to cheer and the train men joined in with a will. Sheridan made prompt use of the timely incident. He sent word to the engineer to keep up whistling and to the train hands to cheer and make such clatter as would imply the arrival of fresh men. The civilians took the hint. There was a pandemonium of yells and huzzas.

"At this moment Sheridan swung his tired battalions into line (virtually all of the men were mounted for this final onslaught). . . . Half a mile in front of them were the grey masses, moving in and out in busy preparation for their final attack. The scene on both sides was a spirited one. To the Federals the moment was big with fate. But there was no time for reflection.

70

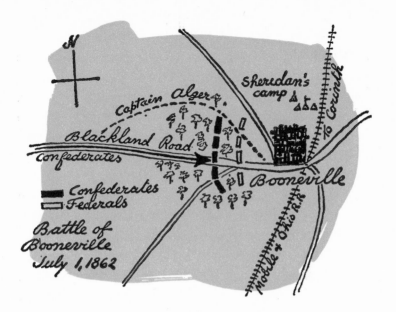

Captain Alger

Sheridan's
camp

Blackland Road

Confederates

■ Confederates
□ Federals

Booneville

to Corinth

Mobile + Ohio R.R.

Battle of
Booneville
July 1, 1862

Sheridan is in front. He shouts to his troopers 'Forward!'
The squadrons sweep across the fields in close order. As
they draw near, shots from the Confederate carbines
and light artillery empty a saddle here and there.

"Still on they go. No one has thought for anything
but the enemy. . . . They draw closer and closer to
the foe. Each bluecoat singles out his man and with a
crash and a yell as of contending demons the two forces
come together. The Confederate line wavers and then
breaks before the force of Sheridan's first charge."

Actually, Alger had lunged into the Confederate rear
like a minor thunderbolt at the same time but could not
come close enough to the Federal lines to be heard or
seen by Sheridan. The attack was a complete surprise to
the enemy. Fearing that the train had brought heavy
reinforcements and believing Alger's force was part of

a larger body of cavalry in their rear, the Confederates broke and fled at every point.

Alger's position continued very perilous, however. The captain and his little command now were rushing to the rear with as much speed as the enemy. They had emptied their revolvers into a confused mass of Confederates which they had driven off a road. The Confederates, greatly superior in numbers, charged, and a running fight ensued, sabers slashing, revolvers and carbines banging. Each side was trying to get away from the other and man by man they separated whenever a by-road or a bit of woods opened a chance for escape.

Alger rode side-by-side with a southern cavalryman, each emptying his revolver at the other without doing any harm. The captain had fired his last shot when his big gray horse, somewhat unmanageable even in calmer moments, galloped out of control into a nearby wood. A branch tore Alger from the saddle and sent him crashing to the ground, the fall breaking several of his ribs. He was picked up late in the day and taken to Sheridan who praised him highly for his valor.

The battle of Booneville was over. A small fray compared to others in the Civil War but a very decisive victory for the Union. Without Phil's quick-thinking it might very well have ended in disastrous defeat. It was reported after the engagement that an old Negro who lived in a hut in the forest west of Booneville contributed to the Union victory. The Negro was contacted by Captain Alger's guide and showed him the best point for an attack against the Confederates.

At 5 P.M., Phil followed his earlier telegram calling for aid with a dispatch to divisional headquarters at Rienzi saying:

"I will not want any infantry supports; I have whipped the enemy today . . . it will be well to let me have a battery of artillery. I might then be able to follow up the enemy."

At dusk, Phil rode through his encampment, a grin creasing his begrimed face, expressing thanks to his men for their gallant conduct. Everywhere his arrival was greeted by cheers and shouts of "Hello, Phil!" "Here comes Little Phil!" and "Hooray for Sheridan!"

Late that night infantry and artillery reinforcements reached Booneville and Sheridan and his brigade were ordered to return to encampments at Rienzi.

The news of the Booneville victory spread fast by telegraph and newspaper accounts, causing a particular stir in Somerset, Ohio. Major General William S. Rosecrans, in command of the Army of the Mississippi, immediately issued a general order to be read to every unit of the army. It praised the "coolness, determination and fearless gallantry" of Colonel Sheridan, his officers and men.

At the end of July five top-ranking commanders, including Rosecrans, signed a petition which was telegraphed to "Old Brains" Halleck, who now was General-in-Chief in Washington. It read:

"Brigadiers scarce. Good ones scarcer . . . undersigned respectfully beg that you will obtain the promotion of Sheridan. He is worth his weight in gold."

73

CHAPTER 7

WARHORSE

The horse which Captain Archibald Campbell of the 2nd Michigan Cavalry led toward Phil's headquarters at Rienzi on a sunny day of August, 1862, would have drawn admiring glances anywhere in the world.

It was a big, black gelding, with flashing eyes and lively gait, its every movement revealing superb muscular power and coordination. Arriving at the headquarters of his commander, Campbell asked to see the colonel. When Phil came out, he smilingly acknowledged the captain's salute. Then he strode up to the horse and gave it a friendly pat on the neck. The horse acknowledged the caress by promptly nuzzling the

74

colonel's chest. Sheridan knew the horse, which belonged to Campbell. He had ridden it on several occasions, but not in action.

"I always like to see and ride this horse, Captain. Did you bring him here for any particular reason today?"

"Yes, sir, I know you like him, I want to give him to you as a present," the captain said. "I really want you to take him."

"This is indeed one of the finest gifts anyone could give me, but what about payment?" said Phil, obviously deeply pleased.

"No, sir, I do not want payment, it is a gift," the captain replied. "It is a good animal, but as you know I never did much riding before the war and prefer a less fiery mount for myself."

"All right, Captain, and my thanks," Phil said.

Phil, whose head barely reached the horse's withers, then jumped on its bare back, seized the bridle and as the animal pranced away shouted back to the captain: "We're doing fine. I'll call him Rienzi, that's it, Rienzi."

That day marked the beginning of a virtually inseparable companionship between Sheridan and this horse. The horse is shown in a steel engraving based on a photograph in Phil's memoirs and is described as follows:

"This horse was of Morgan stock and then about three years old. He was jet black, excepting three white feet, sixteen hands high and strongly built. . . . He was so active that he could cover with ease five miles an hour at his natural walking gait.

"The gelding had been ridden very seldom. Campbell had been unaccustomed to riding till the war broke out and, I think, felt some disinclination to mount the fiery colt. He had an affection for him that never waned, however, and would come often to my headquarters to see his favorite. From the time the horse was presented to me until the close of the war I rode him almost continuously, in every campaign and battle in which I took part. I never found him overcome by fatigue, though on many occasions his strength was severely tested by long marches and short rations.

"I never observed in him any vicious habit; a nervousness and restlessness and switching of the tail when everything around was quiet, being the only indication that he might be untrustworthy. No one but a novice could be deceived by this, however, for the intelligence in his every feature and his thoroughbred appearance were so striking that any person accustomed to horses could see that this was a noble animal."

After Booneville, Sheridan carried out extensive scouting operations. Completing one such trip, studying the movements of the Confederate armies, Sheridan brought back highly important information and conveyed it to Ulysses Grant. It was the first tip-off that Confederate commander Braxton Bragg was preparing an invasion of Kentucky.

"On July 30th I learned from Colonel Ph. H. Sheridan, who had been to the south that Bragg was in person at Rome, Georgia, with his troops moving by rail to

Chattanooga (Tennessee) and his wagon train marching overland to join him at Rome," Grant noted.

By the fall of 1862 Union hopes of bringing the Confederacy to its knees with campaigns in Virginia aimed at Richmond, and attacks in the Mississippi, Tennessee and Cumberland river zones, had evaporated. Various commanders had failed to move with sufficient celerity after hard-won victories such as Fort Donelson, Mill Springs and Shiloh.

Halleck, notably, had failed to chase and destroy retreating Confederate armies. He had moved slowly on Corinth and then had allowed the Confederates to withdraw almost unmolested to another base at Tupelo, due south of Corinth, in Mississippi. Promoted to General-in-Chief, "Old Brains" proceeded as might be expected to blunder anew in his post in Washington. He ordered Don Carlos Buell's Army of the Ohio to move on Chattanooga and Knoxville, Tennessee, not swiftly but slowly, giving the Southerners ample time to organize defenses and deploy troops as they saw fit. In addition, the Union had been shaken by another serious defeat at Bull Run, in the northern area, west of Washington.

The situation was further complicated by the jealous quarrels and intrigue carried on among high and low officers, tearing at the fabric of the Union command and hampering smooth and full coordination of military operations.

Bragg did not waste any time while the Union armies were hesitating. In the fall of '62, he and General E.

Kirby Smith were on the march northward in two columns, grouping forty-seven thousand men, mounted and on foot. The columns were to join up in central Kentucky and move against Louisville, and Cincinnati across the Ohio River. Coincident with Bragg's moves, General Robert E. Lee, top Confederate commander, was heading for Pennsylvania in the more northern zone, confronting the Union with major threats on two widely-separated fronts.

As a result of these developments, Phil, still at Rienzi in Mississippi, was notified that he would be in charge of transporting four Missouri and Illinois infantry regiments, plus his own 2nd Michigan Cavalry, to Louisville.

The troops detrained at Louisville on September 13. Near-panic conditions prevailed in the city as a result of news that Bragg was advancing steadily northward, outmarching and outwitting units of Buell's army.

Shortly after his arrival, Phil was informed that his appointment as brigadier general had been confirmed. He had actually attained this rank on the day of the Booneville battle, since the confirmation said the promotion was effective as July 1, 1862. Phil was moving up the ladder so fast that he was actually outstripping his promotions. He would only be confirmed as a colonel after the war!

On September 29 Phil was appointed commander of the newly-formed 11th Division, part of the 3rd Corps led by General C. C. Gilbert. It was a proud moment for him, tinged with one sharp regret. At this point he had to say good-bye to his cherished "Wolverines," the men of the 2nd Michigan who had provided him with his first important victory at Booneville.

Now Sheridan was in command of infantry, a division numbering some forty-two hundred fighting men backed by two batteries of light artillery. Included in his command were the 35th Brigade, made up of the 44th Illinois, the 73rd Illinois and the 2nd and 5th Missouri; the 36th Brigade, consisting of the 85th, 86th and 125th Illinois and the 52nd Ohio; the 37th Brigade, comprising the 36th and 88th Illinois, the 21st Michigan and the 24th Wisconsin; Battery 1, 2nd Illinois Artillery and Battery G, 1st Missouri Artillery. The stage was ready for a sharp struggle in northern Kentucky. The Confederates under Bragg and Smith had effected a junction at Frankfort but planned to withdraw before Buell could cut off their retreat.

On October 1, Phil, mounted on Rienzi, rode out of Louisville at the head of his division, part of the three columns of the 50,000-man Army of the Ohio advancing on Perryville. After a wearisome march of some seventy miles in uncomfortably hot weather, the northern force reached the Perryville vicinity on the evening of October 7.

Four Confederate divisions—some twenty-four thousand men—already had taken up positions on the heights bordering the nearby Chaplin River. This force had the task of maintaining open roads for the balance of the southern army near Frankfort, thus preventing escape avenues from being cut off.

Neither side actually wanted to fight it out in this area. Buell believed he was confronted by the entire Confederate force and desired to pick another battle site. The Confederates, on the other hand, did not desire to take the offensive, since their orders were merely to keep open the communications southward.

Both armies and their animals, plagued by July heat in October, badly needed water. The Confederates were in a better position in this regard, since they controlled Doctor's Creek, a tributary of the Chaplin River. It was imperative for the Federals to oust them from this area, and Phil's division was picked as spearhead, to attack at "day dawn."

Strolling past the campfires of an Ohio division near his own force that night, Phil halted at a campfire where several officers were conferring. Sheridan started. He recognized one of the men in spite of the fact that his face was older and now boasted a big mustache and a goatee. It was Terrill, the man with whom he had tangled so gravely at West Point. Terrill, a Virginian, had elected from the start of the war to fight for the Union.

"I believe we have met in years past, Brigadier," Phil said with a smile, noting the insignia on the other man's uniform. "I see you now have the same rank as I do. May I shake your hand and let us forget the past and be friends."

Terrill, still much taller than Phil, looked down at him and also grinned. He quickly grasped the outstretched hand and said:

80

"You're darned right I know you. You are Phil Sheridan, and I have heard lots about you, all to the good. You know, I have thought about those days, and have felt many times that I was very wrong in our quarrel. I am very pleased to be your friend henceforth."

Phil chatted with Terrill and other officers present, Colonel Webster and General James Jackson. Then he left for his own headquarters. He would never see them alive again, for all three met their death the following day. To Phil it was always a sad memory. But he was glad that he had "buried the hatchet" on the eve of battle.

At dawn the next day Phil, on his black horse, hurled an assault brigade from his division against the Confederates defending the creek, routing them after a sharp skirmish.

Always a front line fighter, he again showed his ability to think for himself in an emergency and do the right thing. Ignoring repeated orders from General Buell to avoid provoking a major engagement, Phil pushed ahead, after reinforcing his spearhead with other troops and batteries from his division.

"We could not hold the ground unless we occupied a range of hills, called Chaplin Heights (northwest of Perryville), which were in front of the Chaplin River," he recalled.

The heights were seized and immediately Phil had his men dig rifle pits and post artillery in key positions. The move caused alarm at Union headquarters, about a mile behind the front lines, and Buell harried Phil with message after message warning him that he must not bring on a general engagement. Sheridan replied tartly that he was "not bringing on an engagement but that the enemy evidently intended to do so."

Two hours after Chaplin Heights had been taken, the Confederates, waves of men in gray and butternut, their mouths contorted in the fearsome rebel battle yell, stormed against Phil's position. The Confederates, using more than a division, were thrown back in this first attack.

Simultaneously, the Union First Corps, on Phil's left, commanded by General Alexander McCook, moved forward toward the Chaplin River. Phil, from his advance position, could see that the bulk of the Confederate forces was right in McCook's path, across the river. He tried desperately to warn McCook of the danger but could not do so, partly because of the cannon and musket smoke wreathing trees and fields.

Hardly had the Union corps reached the river when the Confederates charged and hurled it back at bayonet point, while Rebel batteries pounded its rear echelons. McCook's men reeled back, suffering heavy casualties.

Phil promptly pushed some of his batteries forward and attempted to help McCook with enfilading fire, but this could not stop the retreat. Finally McCook's troops stood firm, but their divisions were too badly shaken for any further offensive action that day.

Four more heavy assaults were launched by the Confederates against Sheridan's hill position, where the big horse and its rider galloped back and forth.

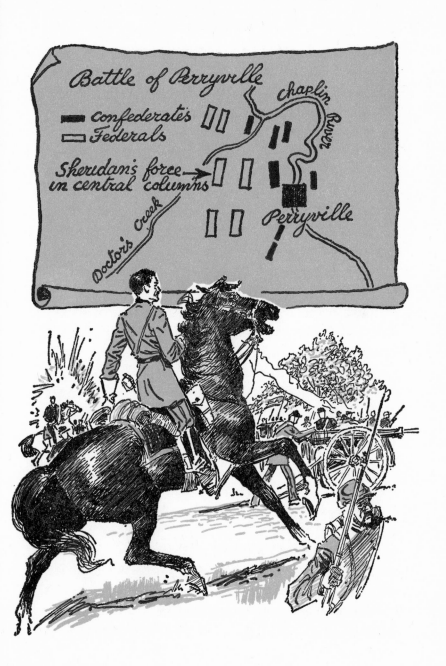

"Give them canister!" Phil shouted to his cannoneers.

The canister—shells filled with small bits of rusty scrap iron, lead balls, slugs and iron pellets—ripped into the enemy, but still the men in gray came on yelling. Several waves reached the rifle pits and bitter hand-to-hand fighting ensued. Sheridan's division held fast. Its heroic stand saved the day and, according to most military historians, prevented four southern divisions from wrecking an entire Union army.

By 4 P.M. the battle of Perryville had ended, the Confederates withdrawing slowly southward. Each side had suffered 5,000 casualties. The heaviest damage was among the Federals in McCook's corps. Phil's division, although it had been the target of most enemy attacks, had sustained only 350 casualties, 44 killed, 292 wounded, 14 missing. The small number of casualties was largely due to the fact that he had ordered the digging of rifle pits and posted his artillery extremely well. Only once before had he commanded artillery, in the West against the Indians, if the small signal cannon used there could be classified as such.

Though they were bone-tired, dusty and dirty, there was not a man of the 11th Division that did not cheer loudly when Phil trotted past them late that afternoon, waving his battered hat. He might be small in size, but there could be no doubt he was a giant in battle. It was noted at this time by the soldiers, as others would later, that Phil's eyes assumed a "reddish glow" in battle as if he burned with some strange inner fire.

Newspapers promptly hailed him as "the paladin of

Perryville." One combat reporter wrote that Sheridan "carried the forked lightnings on the battlefield, his brigades swarming forward under his lead like the mighty nimbus of a storm. . . . Sheridan is more than magnetic, he is electric."

Some newspapers reported that Phil had been killed. When he got hold of the newspapers a few days later, he was pleased to note "that the error had been corrected before my obituary could be written."

The Confederates withdrew in a southeasterly direction. Buell moved after them with his force but so slowly that nothing decisive was accomplished, and he was removed from command.

The army then moved into winter quarters at Nashville, Tennessee, and was placed under Major General William Rosecrans, the same commander who had earlier signed the telegram stating that Sheridan "was worth his weight in gold."

"Old Rosy," as troopers nicknamed him, was a genial man with a big red nose and a hearty laugh. Under his leadership Federal troops had smashed a major Confederate attack led by General Van Dorn against Corinth on October 3 and 4 while Buell's army was moving on Perryville. A West Pointer, he was not a particularly brilliant tactician, but there was no question about his conscientiousness and battle courage.

The Army of the Ohio was now re-designated the Army of the Cumberland and considerably reorganized in October, November and December. Phil's command was affected, becoming the Third Division in Alexander

McCook's corps. Without any reflection on their service, a number of brigade officers were replaced for varying reasons. One of Phil's West Point classmates, Joshua Sill, whom Phil greatly admired, was placed in command of a brigade that had been commanded by Colonel Nicholas Greusel. Another man whom Phil knew from West Point, General George Thomas, one of the Union's best commanders who had taught cavalry tactics at West Point, was placed in command of an army corps under Rosecrans.

During this reorganization, Phil was constantly busy. His men were kept active with drills, rifle and cannon target practice, and scouting expeditions. He also worked to perfect his own intelligence department—known today as *G-2*. At that time there was no organized intelligence grouping in the armies, either North or South. News of enemy intentions, movements and plans was garnered in a more or less haphazard manner. But Phil was always seeking information, and his scouting was well organized.

One day a "small, active, busy man with an intelligent face," an Eastern Tennesseean, volunteered for service with Sheridan. His name was James Card, who stated truthfully that he was intensely loyal to the Union. Engaged in various activities, including book peddling and random preaching, he knew middle and eastern Tennessee and Georgia like the palm of his hand. Phil immediately liked the man and attached him to his division as a scout and guide. Card, acting really as a spy, would remain with Phil for many months, truly invaluable as a supplier of vital information about the enemy.

Phil's G-2 was probably the best organized of any army in the Civil War, with himself as head. "He was always the best informed man in the command as to the enemy," Ulysses Grant subsequently said of him.

He was relentless in questioning any Confederate prisoner he came across, a technique not exploited to its fullest at that time.

"That there man, he'll talk the eyes right out of your head," one southern prisoner remarked after a long questioning session with Phil.

On December 26, 1862—a gloomy day with fields, roads and hills shrouded in a chill mist coupled with intermittent rain—trumpets sounded and "Old Rosy's" regiments moved out of Nashville southeastward toward Murfreesboro. The army on the march numbered forty-three thousand, mostly infantry and artillery, and some cavalry. It was not the best time of year for an offensive, but Washington was anxious for decisive action in this theater. Bragg was at Murfreesboro with a force about the same strength. One of the fiercest engagements of the war was impending, and Sheridan would be in the thick of it.

In his memoirs Phil cites briefly a fearsome peril faced by badly wounded soldiers lying alone in isolated spots in fields or forests, particularly at night. This peril— roving, hungry wild pigs—would attack men too helpless to ward them off.

There were such pigs in the cedars and underbrush just outside Murfreesboro.

CHAPTER **8**

DREAD FIELD

The tree-studded valleys and hillocks just west of
Murfreesboro, Tennessee, were moist and gloomy on
the night of December 30, 1862. A thin winter mist
coiled around the cedar trees or drifted over open fields
in weird arabesques. The air was chill, the dripping
leaves stirred by a sharp winter wind.

The grass and ground everywhere were wet. So were
the overcoats and uniforms of more than 80,000 fighting
men huddled around sputtering campfires or sleeping
under blankets in the open or in tents. There was little
laughter among the men on either side. There could be

no question that dawn would bring battle—one in which there would be plenty of one-way tickets.

In tent hospitals behind the lines, surgeons readied their instruments. These included sharp saws and knives of various types. The amputation "mill" was always busy in battle hours in the Civil War. Where amputation could not be performed and a man was badly wounded, the chance of survival was slim in those days, the menace of gangrene constant. There was no organized corps of stretcher-bearers. Any wounded who were immediately picked up and cared for were very, very lucky men.

The little man restlessly pacing up and down the encampments of the Third Division was in a state of sharp alert. Nothing of importance escaped his eyes as he strode by infantry bivouacs and artillery emplacements. Puffing on a small, curved meerschaum pipe he had cherished from West Point days, he would occasionally stop and peer eastward into the darkness where the enemy rested in the cedar brake, along Stones River.

Philip Sheridan's face was grim. He feared that Rosecrans' tactical plan—to strike with the left wing and hold back with the right—might suffer an upset. Bragg, whose force was encamped less than a mile away, planned to do the same thing, using his left for a hammer blow. But the Federals did not know this, not even Phil, although he intuitively feared it.

"During the evening of the 30th, feeling keenly all the solicitude which attends one in anticipation of a battle, I examined my position with great care, inspecting its whole length several times to remedy any defects that might exist and to let the men see that I was alive to their interests and advantages," Phil wrote. "After dark, I went back to the rear of my reserve brigade and established my headquarters behind the trunk of a large, fallen tree. Sheltered somewhat by this tree from the cold December wind, I lay down beside a small campfire to get some rest."

The positions of the Federals and the Confederates on that night were practically the same as shown on the battle map. Phil's Division was part of McCook's right wing.

Before midnight, Rosecrans evolved a plan aimed at making the enemy believe the Federal right wing extended much farther than it did. Campfires were lit for some distance beyond the tip of the right wing. This plan would backfire, prompting Bragg's tough and clever Lt. Gen. William Hardee merely to make a wider encircling move, with bad results for "Old Rosy's" men.

"Long before dawn my division breakfasted and was assembled, the cannoneers at their pieces," the memoirs continue. "While we were thus preparing, all the recent signs of activity in the enemy's camp (this activity had been noted by Sheridan about 2 A.M.) was hushed and a death-like stillness prevailed in the cedars to our front."

At 7 A.M. the Confederates struck first in massive waves, with assault troops commanded by Hardee crashing against the Federal right. Sheridan, astride Rienzi, and Sill and other mounted officers took up positions just behind the lines of his division.

The Southerners came on at a dead run, bayonets leveled, as artillery roared on both sides, their red flags fluttering under the lowering sky. Several regiments went straight for the Third Division, but the bulk of the attackers swept toward regiments on the extreme right under Union brigadiers Johnson and Davis.

Three of Sheridan's artillery batteries opened up, eighteen pieces belching fire from a commanding position which Phil had carefully selected.

"The effect of the fire on the advancing column was terrible. But it continued on till it reached the edge of the timber where Sill's right lay, when my infantry opened up at a range of not over fifty yards. For a short time the Confederates withstood the fire but then wavered, broke and fell back toward their original lines.

"As they retired, Sill's brigade followed them in a spirited charge, driving them back across the open ground and behind their entrenchments. In this charge the gallant Sill was killed, a rifle ball passing through his upper lip and penetrating the brain . . . this repulse gave us an hour's time. . . . I recalled the brigade to its original position, for the turning column on my right (the Confederates attacking the extreme Federal right) was now assuming a most menacing attitude and it was urgently necessary to prepare for it. . . ."

The situation on the Federal right was more than menacing, it was catastrophic.

The Johnson and Davis regiments, not aroused as early as those of Sheridan, were still yawning and rubbing the sleep out of their eyes when they suddenly beheld an appalling horde of enemies coming at them full tilt from the south. Within an hour all of McCook's right wing, except for Sheridan, had collapsed, its men withdrawing in disorder, many of them fleeing to the rear through Sheridan's lines.

On orders from Rosecrans, Phil promptly shifted his brigades in a right angle, stationing his men along the edge of the Round Forest. Meanwhile, Thomas regrouped the Federal center to meet the Confederate threat.

One of the bitterest and most bloody contests of that fearful day now took place at the edge of the forest.

Time and again the Confederates, flushed with initial victory, confident that a Federal disaster was at hand, surged against Phil's positions. The Third Division could not be routed, making a stand seldom rivaled in military annals, certainly not surpassed in heroism by any in the Civil War.

Opposing artillery dueled at distances of not over two hundred yards. A private named Daggett serving in one of Phil's regiments recorded:

"A few of the more venturesome Rebels reached a rail fence less than twenty yards from the muzzles of our muskets, but none ever returned. Others paused at a distance of 75 to 100 yards, delivered their fire and dropped to the ground to load and fire again.

"Others came up in their rear but no human endurance could withstand the murderous fire poured into them from our well-protected line, reinforced now on the right and left by other troops who had rallied to our assistance. . . ."

Eventually, toward noon, Phil was ordered to pull back through the forest and join the bulk of the Federal forces now grouped along the Nashville and Chattanooga Railway embankment and the Nashville turnpike. The major reason for the withdrawal was that Phil's ammunition was almost depleted.

Fighting constantly, Phil's division withdrew in order. Eight guns and many seriously wounded men had to be left behind in the forest.

Waving his sword, shouting orders or words of encouragement, Sheridan was always on the move where the withdrawal action was heaviest. His horse, which had not been in any major action before, proved itself a born war charger, obedient to the reins, quick of hoof, excited but never out of control.

The fighting was by no means over for Phil and the other Federals. Aligned in a new arrowhead formation, right and left wings almost back to back, the Union soldiers had to beat off repeated assaults. Phil's men were involved in some of the fiercest struggles.

"Old Rosy" also was seen riding everywhere, not staying in one spot more than half an hour, according to one officer who rode with him. Shortly after Sheridan had taken up his new position, Rosecrans rode up with some of his orderlies and several officers to inspect the new alignment of these and other regiments.

"As he passed to the open ground on my left, I joined him," Phil wrote. "The enemy, seeing this mounted party, turned his guns upon it. His accurate aim was soon rewarded, for a solid shot carried away the head of Colonel Garesche, Rosecrans' chief-of-staff, and wounded two or three orderlies. Garesche's appalling death stunned us all. A momentary expression of horror came over Rosecrans' face but at such a time the importance of self-control was vital. He pursued his course with apparent indifference, which we knew was assumed for he undoubtedly was most sorrowful over the death of his staff officer."

Finally at dusk, with rain falling, the fighting generally halted. It had been going on practically without stop for ten hours. Some twenty thousand men, about the same number on each side, had been killed, wounded or would be declared missing. Throughout the sodden night the forests and thickets re-echoed to the groans and cries of the wounded, pleading for water, for help, and for rescue from the vicious, hungry pigs.

That night Rosecrans called a conference of all his top commanders to decide whether his army should stand and continue the battle or withdraw to Nashville. It was a weird "summit" conference, with begrimed faces and muddy, torn uniforms illuminated by firelight.

Rosecrans vacillated, receiving varied opinions. Thomas, hearing the word "retreat" too often, suddenly bridled and said: "Gentlemen, I know of no better place to die than right here."

Phil immediately ranged himself beside the Virginian and said crisply:

"I request for my division the honor of leading the attack tomorrow."

It was decided there would be no retreat.

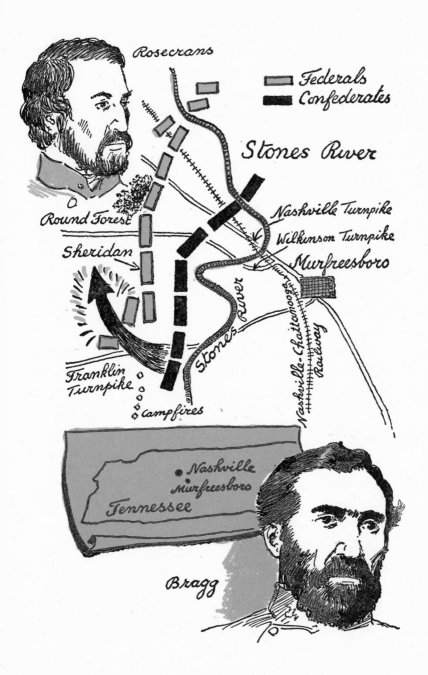

"As soon as possible after the lull I went over the battlefield to collect such of my wounded as had not been carried off to the south and to bury my dead," Sheridan wrote in his diary. "In the cedars and ground where I had been so fiercely assaulted . . . the dead had nearly all been left unburied but as there was a likelihood of their mutilation by roving swine, the bodies had mostly been collected in piles at different points and enclosed by fences."

His division had suffered more than any other in the Union lines. Its casualties totaled 1,633 out of a pre-battle strength of 4,164: 237 killed, 989 wounded and 407 missing. The killed included four brigade commanders. It is said Phil cried when he reported his losses to Rosecrans that night.

Actually, the Battle of Stones River ended at dusk, December 31. The next day Confederates made several small-scale attacks but nothing changed. By January 2, Bragg withdrew from Murfreesboro, harried by Federal cavalry and artillery.

The battle, costly as it was, gave a much-needed boost to Northern morale and strengthened the government's position abroad, notably in England and France. It offered a new ray of hope to heavily-burdened Abraham Lincoln, then about to issue one of the most important declarations of his entire career: The Emancipation Proclamation on Negro Slavery.

"Bragg came near destroying us," Phil commented. "Had he done so Nashville would probably have fallen; at all events Kentucky would have been opened again to his incursions and the theater of war very likely transferred once more to the Ohio River." As the case now stood, however, Nashville was firmly established as a base for future operations; Kentucky was safe, and Bragg, thrown on the defensive, was compelled to give his thoughts to the protection of the interior of the Confederacy and the security of Chattanooga, rather than indulge in schemes of conquest north of the Cumberland River.

It would be near Chattanooga, along a stream called by the Indians "River of Death," that Phil would face his next big battle. The stream is listed on maps as Chickamauga Creek.

CHAPTER 9

RIVER OF DEATH

For the Army of the Cumberland there now came
a battle lull, roughly from January to the end of June,
1863. Things were quiet except for scattered engagements with enemy cavalry along communications and
scouting patrols.

In April Phil was promoted to Major General for
his distinguished services at Perryville and Stones River.
On this occasion, his officers dug into their pockets to
the tune of $2,000 and gave their diminutive com-
mander a fine present; an ornate saber, two silver-
mounted Colt revolvers and a superb saddle for Rienzi.

This token of affection and admiration stirred Phil deeply.

Prodded by Washington, Rosecrans got his army on the move again in June, 1863. In infantry, cavalry, and artillery, it totaled close to fifty-six thousand. The objective this time was the city of Chattanooga, Tennessee, literally the gateway to the southeastern portion of the Confederacy, at that moment its most vital strategic point. It was only fifty miles southeast of Murfreesboro as the crow flies, but high, rugged mountain terrain lay between the two points.

Heavy rains fell during the advance southeastward. Roads became seas of mud and at times Phil and his men had to struggle through swollen mountain torrents up to their armpits in water, many of them swept to their deaths in the currents. Hordes of men in his and other divisions had to help horses pull artillery up steep mountainsides, lathered with oozing mud.

Constant attacks by Confederate cavalry and infantry harried the Union troops as Bragg's armies withdrew toward Chattanooga. After weeks of marching, counter-marching and maneuvering the two armies were lined up in battle array just west of Chickamauga Creek, after Federal pressure had forced Confederate withdrawal from Chattanooga.

The battle of Chickamauga opened September 19 with a series of sharp but indecisive Confederate probing assaults. By nightfall of that day Rosecrans and his officers were uneasy. They feared that Bragg had led them into a trap. Their uneasiness was not in any way lessened by reports that powerful reinforcements had been obtained by Bragg. This was true. His force was nearing the 70,000-man mark. It would be the first time in the war that the South faced the North with considerable numerical superiority in a major battle. For Phil the events of the morrow would have a particularly nightmarish resemblance to the situation at Stones River. His division's position on the night of the nineteenth was close to the tip of the Federal right, with tumbled, hilly terrain behind him and his men.

Eerie, almost impenetrable fog enveloped the battle zone on the morning of September 20, the masses of soldiers spectral in the gloom. When the fog lifted in mid-morning, the great battle was opened with a Confederate smash against the Federal left under Thomas. His divisions stood firm and their great stand that day would forever make the doughty Virginian known as "The Rock of Chickamauga." Then a grave Union blunder occurred on orders from Rosecrans. A veteran division, just to the right of the Federal center, was ordered to withdraw and move to the support of the left. Just opposite this gap was a powerful Confederate force under the great commander James Longstreet, with orders to attack the Federal right.

About noontime, Longstreet sent his veteran brigades in a crashing blow against the central Federal lines as heavy fighting continued in the sector held by Thomas. Taking advantage of the gap, Longstreet's thunderbolt drove through, and the Army of the Cumberland was cut in half. Regiments and divisions cracked before the

To Chattanooga, 5 miles

Rossville

Horseshoe Ridge

Thomas

Lookout Mt.

Missionary Ridge

West Chickamauga Creek

Sheridan

Confederate breakthrough

Tennessee

Nashville
Murfreesboro

Chattanooga

Chickamauga

ferocious onslaught and streamed toward Rossville in utter confusion.

Sheridan and his men were in the thick of the fighting and contested the ground stubbornly as Longstreet's punch widened, but eventually had to withdraw in the midst of mounting chaos. He pulled back and headed for Rossville, planning to reinforce Thomas. He kept his division in reasonably good order in spite of terrible losses and did effect contact with Thomas late in the day.

Thomas' immortal stand at Horseshoe Ridge where he was virtually encircled prevented complete destruction of the Army of the Cumberland.

When the fighting ended at nightfall the casualty toll was staggering: twenty-three thousand Confederates and sixteen thousand Federals killed, wounded or missing. Unable to crush Thomas, the Southerners were too exhausted and too shaken by their losses to continue any massive assaults. It was a big victory but too costly a one for a Confederacy beginning to writhe under ever-mounting Union hammer blows by sea, by river and by land, including Federal victories at Vicksburg and Gettysburg.

Late that night, an exhausted Phil dismounted from an equally tired Rienzi in a clump of trees near Rossville. As an orderly took charge of the horse, which had been unsaddled, "I lay down at the foot of a tree with my saddle for a pillow and a saddle-blanket for a cover.

"Some soldiers near me having built a fire, were making coffee, and I guess I must have been looking on wistfully, for in a little while they brought me a tin-cupful of the coffee and a small piece of hard bread, which I relished keenly, it being the first food that had passed my lips since the night before. . . . I was very discouraged. . . . I had been obliged to fight my command under the most disadvantageous circumstances, in disconnected positions, without supports, without even opportunity to form in line of battle and at one time contending against four enemy divisions.

"In this battle of Chickamauga, out of an effective strength of 4,000 bayonets, I had lost 1,517 officers and men, including two brigade commanders."

"Old Rosy," who would shortly be succeeded in command by Thomas, would be haunted by the terrible shadow of Chickamauga for the remaining thirty years of his life.

CHAPTER **10**

THE INCREDIBLE ASSAULT

The tactical plan of Ulysses Grant on November 25, 1863, was along classic military lines—a double envelopment striking to the right and left with harassing action against the enemy's center.

His target was Missionary Ridge, to the east of Chattanooga. The ridge, running from southwest to northeast, had a height of five hundred feet in most sectors. Its steep rocky slopes were honeycombed with gullies and littered with sparse trees and underbrush. By November 25, Bragg's Confederates had transformed the ridge into a formidable bastion.

What occurred on November 25 probably is unique

in military annals. It had all the earmarks of a theatrical spectacular in a vast natural amphitheater with an awe-inspiring climax. Before it ended imperturbable Grant would almost bite his big cigar in two with surprise and have a new conception of the kind of stuff the men of the Army of the Cumberland were made of. Fiery Phil was destined to play a primary role that day, one of the most exciting in his life. In the final act he would caper and yell like a boy, some twenty thousand other men joining him in wild jubilation. On this day all classic military concepts went up in smoke.

The weeks following Chickamauga were bitter for the Army of the Cumberland. After the defeat, Rosecrans pulled his army back into Chattanooga, and what was bound to happen did occur. Bragg besieged the army. Supplies began to dwindle, for they could only be funneled in through a very narrow and difficult passage. Near-starvation prevailed in the Federal camps while the Southerners, prodding them with artillery, waited calmly for the enemy to give up from sheer hunger and despair.

Meanwhile, the slopes of Missionary Ridge facing Chattanooga were fortified, rifle pits dug at the base, another line of pits half-way up and artillery and more troops on the crest. By November it was the most formidable natural fortified bastion held by any army in the Civil War.

Fortunately for the Union, Washington, badly shaken by Chickamauga, almost immediately took steps to relieve the Cumberlanders. Grant, who had captured

Vicksburg, was ordered to proceed to Chattanooga as commander of all Federal operations between the Alleghenies and the Mississippi. Reinforcements numbering some thirty thousand men from Grant's Army of the Tennessee and the Army of the Potomac were rushed to the beleaguered Cumberlanders.

Late in October, Grant, nursing a leg painfully hurt in a fall from his horse, arrived in Chattanooga. General Joe Hooker with the Army of the Potomac broke the siege ring near Lookout Mountain and communications were restored. Shortly thereafter General W. T. Sherman arrived with reinforcements from the Army of the Tennessee.

Two of Phil's old friends from West Point days were now in the battle zone. They were George Crook, commanding an Ohio cavalry contingent, and Henry Slocum, who had helped Phil with his studies, commanding a Potomac Army corps.

In a shuffle of the command, Grant replaced Rosecrans with Thomas, the "Rock of Chickamauga," who thus became Phil's direct superior commander. By November 20, Grant, who now had the cream of Federal commanders under him—Sherman, Thomas, Hooker and Sheridan—had perfected his plans.

The opening move came on November 23 when General Woods' division of the Army of the Cumberland, with Sheridan's division in support, surged forward and seized Orchard Knob. The Confederates, who had used it as an outpost, withdrew to Missionary Ridge after a brief skirmish.

In accordance with Grant's plan for a double envelopment aimed at encirclement of Missionary Ridge, Hooker struck at Lookout Mountain on the twenty-fourth. The Confederates, badly outnumbered, were forced to abandon it in an engagement which newspapers called "the battle in the clouds," according it undue importance. At the same time Sherman and his divisions drove against the other end of Missionary Ridge. They were stalled in bitter fighting.

On the twenty-fifth the Federal operation was resumed at dawn, Hooker moving across Chattanooga Valley, his advance hindered by difficult terrain and the swollen waters of Chattanooga Creek. Sherman attacked again but could make little headway.

Sheridan and other Cumberlanders remained in the center, in the immediate vicinity of Orchard Knob. Grant, Thomas, other high commanders, and Assistant Secretary of War Charles Dana were stationed on the knob, which made an excellent vantage point for watching operations. The surprise of the day—which was clear and crisp—would occur right in front of them.

A fine head of steaming anger had been built up in the hearts of the Cumberlanders. For weeks the memory of Chickamauga had rankled both officers and troops. Now it was clear to Phil and all the Cumberlanders that the reinforcements from other armies sent to rescue them would do all the major acting. Theirs would just be a bit part in the center, some limited operation designed to draw Bragg's attention away from his flanks. Grant did indeed have such a plan in mind, for he had some doubts as to the fighting spirit of an army so badly battered a few weeks before.

Shortly after 3 p.m. as valleys and hills shook to the thunder of guns, Grant ordered twenty thousand assault troops of the Cumberlanders to advance and seize the rifle pits at the base of Missionary Ridge. These rifle pits were just opposite the knob, separated from it by open ground, varying in breadth from seven hundred to nine hundred yards. Directly above, Bragg had established his headquarters on the crest, in the center of his line.

Phil's division, now grouping six thousand men, was one of the two in front, and two others followed in support. Every man in the divisions was "crazy to charge," to do something to avenge Chickamauga. Even teamsters and cooks, not called upon to participate in such assaults, had seized muskets and ammunition and joined the ranks.

At 3:40 p.m. the signal guns banged and the assault infantry swept forward, like a blue tide, first at normal marching pace, then at the double, then still quicker, sixty Confederate cannons thundering from the mountain in front of them, Confederate sharpshooters firing without cease. A dirty white cloud of cannon smoke swirled over the top of Missionary Ridge as the guns fired. Through an atmospheric quirk each shot could be seen by the advancing Federals from the moment it left a gun's muzzle.

Phil, mounted on Rienzi, was in the forefront of his troops, conspicuous in blue dress uniform, being field officer of the day at this moment. Unstoppable, the attack divisions swarmed into the rifle pits, sending the Confederates scrambling up to the secondary defense line about midway up the slope.

Grant's orders had been clear—seize the pits and stop. He had no intention of trying an all-out assault against that formidable slope. But the position in these rifle pits was virtually untenable, completely "zeroed in" by Confederate batteries.

To withdraw was unthinkable to any Cumberlander. Stirred by an extraordinary battle fervor, the men simply took matters into their own hands and went on and up, crouching, crawling, panting, yelling. They were an inexorable avalanche in reverse, a frightening sight with their regimental flags waving in the van. Phil and other officers, feeling that this was probably the best move in spite of superior orders, did not order any halt and joined in the assault.

Just before the upward advance, Phil took a gulp of whisky from a small silver flask he carried in his pocket. Then, looking beyond Rienzi's bobbing ears, he gazed upward at Confederate officers in the Thurman house, Bragg's headquarters on the crest. He waved his flask aloft and shouted something unprintable in the Confederates' direction. Although his words could not be heard by those above, the defiance was clear and they knew who the little man was.

Near the Thurman house was a well-known Confederate artillery unit known as the "Churchbell Battery." Its guns, nicknamed Lady Breckenridge, Lady

Bragg and the like, had been cast from bells contributed by the churches of Atlanta. Confederate officers snapped orders and the guns bellowed, aimed at the little gamecock below. The missiles almost got him, spattering dirt on the heaving flanks of Rienzi and Phil's gay uniform. Phil's eyes darkened with fury.

"That was not generous. I'll take those guns for that, you——," he shouted, hurling the flask in the direction of the enemy positions. Then he spurred Rienzi forward and yelled to his men to follow him as the whole line moved upward.

Fortunately for the Federals, the enemy artillery could not be trained too effectively on the attackers once they had seized the middle defense line on the slope.

Back on Orchard Knob, Ulysses Grant bit hard on his cigar. What was afoot? This was incredible and against orders. Turning to Thomas, who was equally surprised, Grant said sharply:

"Did you order those men to go to the top?"

Thomas replied that he had not. Grant then shot the same question at General Gordon Granger, commanding one of Thomas' corps. Granger, visibly deeply stirred by the turn of events, said he had not, but added with some pride that once the boys of the Cumberland Army got going it was "hellishly" hard to stop them.

Grant muttered that someone would get it in the neck if this advance turned into disaster and then again turned his eyes on the hill.

"The enemy's fire from the crest during the ascent was terrific as to noise but as it was plunging it overshot its marks and had little effect on those above the second line of pits," Phil recalled in his memoirs.

Undismayed by losses incurred principally from Confederate musketry fire, the Cumberlanders moved upward. Nearing the top, Phil was obliged to dismount temporarily and advance on foot with his men. At one point a trumpeter whose leg had been shot off below the knee continued blowing his instrument until he fell unconscious. A Confederate officer, refusing to withdraw, drew his sword and prepared to battle with the first Yankee he met. An Indiana private made for him with bayoneted rifle. Just before he reached the officer, he dropped his rifle and went for him with his bare hands in an ape-like crouch. His appearance was so ferocious that the officer was unnerved and took off for a safer area.

"Now mass psychology began to work on the Confederate side," according to R. Ernest Dupuy and Trevor N. Dupuy in their book *The Compact History of the Civil War*. "As they watched the vast panorama spread beneath them, the great lines of troops advancing with apparently unstoppable ardor, their bayonets twinkling in the setting sun, Southern veterans were seized by a panic they had never before experienced. Suddenly the gray clad soldiers began to jump out of their trenches, to run over the crest of the ridge and down on the far side. Bragg and his other officers vainly tried to check this tide of disaster. In a few minutes it was all over (at the crest) with most of the Confederate army, officers and men running away in terror, sweeping Bragg and his staff along with them."

Soon the crest was swarming with wildly shouting, cheering Federals. Sheridan joined in the capers, at one point climbing on one of the "Churchbell" batteries, waving his sword aloft and shouting, "I told them I'd get these guns and we did!"

The Battle of Chattanooga—perhaps better named the Battle of Missionary Ridge—was over. A two-mile hole in his center, Bragg could do nothing but retreat into Georgia. Phil Sheridan went after him with his division but he was the only one to do so, and the pursuit did not develop into anything more than a harrying operation.

"In the action (against Missionary Ridge) I lost 123 officers and 1,181 men killed and wounded," Sheridan wrote. "This was one-third of the casualties suffered by all Union troops that day. My division captured 1,762 prisoners and, in all, 17 pieces of artillery."

"The storming of the ridge by our troops was one of the greatest miracles of military history," Assistant Secretary of War Dana wired Washington the evening of the 25th. . . . "It seems as awful as a visible interposition of God."

Naturally, the Cumberlanders were not reprimanded for their actions, since they had decisively won the day. There were plaudits from Grant, Granger and Thomas. In all likelihood during days following the battle, Grant had time to ponder proverbs dealing with mice and men and such sayings as "man proposes, God disposes."

Chickamauga was a supreme last effort by the Confederacy to achieve a great victory. The Federal army had not been destroyed, however, and Missionary Ridge was a disaster. From now on, the South, like a tiring boxer, could only hope to parry the blows of the Union. The Federal juggernaut in a few months would have 533,000 officers and men in the 1,200-mile battle line extending from the Atlantic to the Rio Grande.

During December, 1863, and the early months of 1864, fighting of an inconclusive nature continued in Tennessee. Phil did not play any signal part in this campaigning, he and his troops being mostly in winter quarters at Loudon. Early in 1864 he took his first leave of absence since 1853 and went north. His memoirs do not state whether he visited Somerset.

Heavier responsibilities were in the offing for both Phil and Grant. On March 12, 1864, Grant was appointed general-in-chief of the Union Armies, replacing Halleck. When Phil, who had gone home on leave, returned to winter headquarters near Chattanooga, he received a telegram from Grant, by then in Washington. Dated March 23, it said:

"Lieutenant General Grant directs that Major General Sheridan immediately repair to Washington and report to the adjutant-general of the army."

Phil knew that this meant farewell to his division for which he had great affection. When he left for Chattanooga and the north, he could not bring himself to bid a formal farewell to his men; his regret at leaving them was too great. But the men gathered on a hill near the railway station and gave Phil thunderous cheers as his train pulled out.

Phil, now thirty-three years old, learned from Thomas at Chattanooga what the telegram was all about. He was to be appointed Chief of Cavalry, Army of the Potomac, which comprised some twelve thousand men in three divisions, the largest cavalry group in the Union armies. There was still plenty of dangerous work ahead for Phil and Rienzi.

CHAPTER **11**

SQUADRONS CHARGE!

President Lincoln had a rare gift for humorous, trenchant comments. Shortly after the tall president met his little cavalryman in Washington in April, 1864, a government official asked him for a description of Sheridan.

"I will tell you just what kind of a chap he is," the President said. "He is one of those long-armed fellows with short legs that can scratch his shins without having to stoop over."

Phil arrived in Washington on April 4 by train. Rienzi traveled with him in a car allocated to animal transportation. With him he brought a staff of three officers. The principal officer was Captain James W. Forsyth, an old friend who had served in the Peninsula and Antietam campaigns under McClellan. This officer knew the ground over which the eastern forces were fighting and was familiar with the Army of the Potomac and the characteristics of its various officers. Such knowledge is often as valuable to a new commander as detailed knowledge of the enemy.

Phil's brother, Michael, now a lieutenant, and Lt. T. W. C. Moore were his two aides-de-camp. They would be faithful companions to Phil for many years, both in peace and war.

After conferring with Halleck, now Grant's Chief-of-Staff, Sheridan met Secretary of War Edwin Stanton, who was chilly and formal, and then saw the President, who was cordial. On April 5 he proceeded by train to Culpeper Court House, Virginia. This was the headquarters of the Army of the Potomac, and Grant was also on the train. During the trip Grant told Phil that he intended to be with that army in impending operations against Robert E. Lee and the Army of Northern Virginia.

"In one month, Phil, all the armies of the Union will be in motion against the enemy, under my general direction," Grant said. "For the first time since the war began, the Confederates will be under attack from all quarters and unable to use interior lines of communication to full advantage. This time we are out to crush our foes once and for all."

The evening of that day, Sheridan formally assumed

command of the twelve thousand cavalrymen encamped at Brandy Station. The men were in fine condition but not so the horses. The reason was that in this army, as in other Union forces, cavalry was not used to its best advantage. The cavalrymen's mounts became exhausted with constant picket and escort duty. Cavalry was considered a sort of adjunct to the infantry and not a powerful force which could be used independently to strike major blows on its own. The Confederates, on the other hand, were much more skillful in use of mounted men and saw to it that their horses got adequate rest prior to any battle or campaign.

Phil had his own ideas on this matter and had to do some verbal sparring with General George Gordon Meade, commander of the army, before he won his major points. His stand would prove spectacularly correct in a few weeks.

Meade countered that if the cavalry were relieved of guard duty infantry columns and supply convoys would be wide open to enemy assaults, especially by cavalry.

"I assured him that with a mass of 10,000 mounted men I could make it so lively for the enemy's cavalry that . . . the flanks and the rear of the Army of the Potomac would require little or no defense," Phil wrote.

Sheridan convinced him that the cavalry should be relieved of unnecessary guard duty so that the horses would be rested and capable of sustained effort in coming operations in the difficult Wilderness terrain.

Phil, who replaced General Alfred Pleasanton in command, was generally pleased with the staff then in existence, notably the three divisional commanders: Brig. Gen. Alfred T. A. Torbert, Brigadier General David McMurtrie Gregg, and Brigadier General James H. Wilson, all veterans of various campaigns. One of the brigade commanders in the Torbert division was a slim young man with a flowing blonde mustache, long yellow hair and a fine opinion of himself. His name was General George Armstrong Custer. He would fight well under Sheridan, but would not be so successful years later against the plains Indians.

As could be expected, Phil proceeded to bring his big command into the best possible shape and drummed into his officers' heads the plans he had formulated. At the same time he closely studied the topography of the Virginia Wilderness terrain and all reports on the disposition of Lee's troops in that area.

In daylight hours and even late at night, the cavalrymen could see Phil riding around on Rienzi, now followed by a mounted orderly bearing his swallow-tailed guidon. His inspection tours covered everything vital, from pup tents to supply wagons and sanitation. His presence alone infused new spirit into cavalry divisions grown listless with dull rounds of duty. All the men longed for action. Where Phil came, action followed.

On May 3 and 4, Grant sent the Army of the Potomac—105,000 men, grouping infantry, cavalry and artillery—across the Rapidan River into the Wilderness. This was an almost impassable area of dense forests, ravines, creeks, and thickets, having no roads worthy of the name.

In this area west of Fredericksburg and about forty-five miles north of Richmond were the mighty Lee and some sixty thousand to seventy thousand Confederate veterans. Lee's cavalry was under one of the South's greatest cavaliers—bearded, handsome J. E. B. Stuart. In the Wilderness, Stuart would meet his equal—the 115 pound thunderbolt from Somerset, Ohio.

Phil and his men were at Todd's Tavern on May 6 while the Battle of the Wilderness raged just south of the Rapidan. His position on the Union left was attacked by Stuart's cavalry, but he met the enemy with his troops dismounted and beat them off.

Then Meade—still stubbornly holding to many of his ideas about cavalry—ordered Phil to withdraw from Todd's Tavern. Stuart, believing Sheridan was in full retreat, went after him like a timber wolf and struck on the night of May 6–7. Custer's brigade attacked in a swirling charge and then the rest of Phil's men hammered Stuart, throwing the Confederates back in confusion to Spotsylvania Courthouse.

As Grant moved in the direction of Spotsylvania Courthouse, one of Phil's divisions drew ahead in a quick night ride and seized it. They were immediately attacked and were about to be reinforced by Phil when Meade interfered. He did not believe that cavalry could hold such a point and ordered it withdrawn, to be replaced by infantry. This created confusion, and as a result the town was in Confederate hands when the prolonged and bloody battle of Spotsylvania started on May 9–10.

Inevitably, Phil and Meade clashed. On May 8 there was a violet argument between them at Meade's head-quarters. Meade charged that Sheridan's actions had pro-voked confusion, and Phil said bluntly that his cavalry was being rendered "inefficient and useless." He capped this by declaring that he could whip Stuart if Meade "would only let him." If, however, Meade insisted on giving the cavalry directions without consulting him or even notifying him, "he (Meade) could henceforth command the Cavalry Corps himself, I would not give it another order," Phil said.

Meade immediately proceeded to Grant's head-quarters to repeat Phil's statements, which Meade felt bordered on insubordination. Finally he told of Sheri-dan's boast that he could trounce Stuart and his cavalry-men if Army of the Potomac horsemen were let loose. If Meade hoped that Grant would rebuke Phil, he was quickly disenchanted. Grant took a couple of puffs from his cigar, recalling that Sheridan was a man who kept promises.

"Did he say that?" he muttered. "Well, if he feels that way let him go and do it."

Almost immediately Phil received orders to proceed with all available mounted men southward, to attack and knock out the Stuart cavalry, wreck communica-tions, and destroy or capture supplies in Lee's rear. The thrust was a bold conception, fifty miles southward to Haxall's Landing, southeast of Richmond, and then north again. The two greatest cavalrymen of the North and South would be the main duelists.

"We are going to fight Stuart's cavalry in consequence of a suggestion I have made," Phil told his officers. "We will give him a fair, square fight. . . . I shall expect nothing but success."

At dawn, May 9, bugles echoed near Aldrich's Station, close to Spotsylvania, and Phil, mounted on Rienzi, led his column along Telegraph Road leading from Fredericksburg to Richmond. The column was miles long, ten thousand cavalrymen riding four abreast in disciplined array, harnesses jingling, saddles creaking, pack mules braying. Hundreds of guidons and flags whipped in the morning breeze, Phil's red-and-white guidon with its twin stars in the van. The Sheridan touch was in evidence from the start. There was no fast trotting or galloping as in previous raids. The advance was at a slow pace, the men dismounting and walking alongside their horses at regular intervals to further spare their animals.

"We saw 'Little Phil' daily, whether we were ahead, in the center or rear of the column," one of his troopers recalled. "We knew we had a thundering good leader and it was a great feeling. He had no uppish ways, always easy and friendly. He'd as soon borrow a light for his pipe from an enlisted man as from an officer."

In rapid succession the cavalry crossed the Ny, Po and Ta rivers, without meeting any opposition. This fact removed "all anxiety about the possibility of passing around Lee's army."

The first major blow was struck at dusk when the column reached the North Anna River. Here Union troopers, with Custer whooping in the lead, fell on Beaver Dam railway depot, routing the guards and freeing 378 Union war prisoners on their way to prison camps. That night they made a mighty bonfire of three large trains, destroying a huge quantity of rations—enough to keep the Lee army fed for twenty days—and valuable medical stores. Tracks south of the station were torn up and telegraph connections wrecked for a distance of ten miles.

During the advance, some of Stuart's forces attacked the column in harassing raids but were beaten off. Bearded "Jeb" first thought of attacking at Beaver Dam in force but then became nervous about Richmond and moved south to keep his force between that vital city and Sheridan. On the evening of May 11, Phil's intelligence information—which he garnered as assiduously as ever—convinced him that Stuart was concentrating his cavalry at Yellow Tavern, only six miles north of Richmond. It was correct.

Here Stuart planned a stand with a shrewd-tactical operation. If Phil should attack Richmond's defenses, Stuart hoped to catch him in the rear. At the same time Phil would be attacked frontally by the four to five thousand troops under General Bragg, now commanding the city's defenses.

Sheridan did not attack the city but stabbed straight at Stuart at Yellow Tavern on May 11, 1864.

Mounted and dismounted, the Union cavalrymen swarmed through the Confederate first line in brisk fighting. Led by Stuart in person, the Confederates then launched a flanking onslaught against the advancing Federals, but Phil anticipated such a move. A lightning attack by Custer's division nullified this assault. While fighting seesawed up and down the line, one of Custer's men, a very lethal marksman, carefully aimed his six-shooter and fired. His target was Stuart, riding in the smoke, encouraging his men with loud shouts.

The .44-caliber bullet ripped into Jeb's abdomen. Mortally wounded, he was taken from the field and transported to Richmond. He lay half delirious through the night in the home of a physician while churchbells rang somberly in the city, warning that the enemy was near. Shortly after dawn, at 7:28 A.M., the South's great cavalry leader, one of the outstanding heroes of the war, went on his last journey. The blow was a shattering one to Lee and the entire Confederacy.

After Stuart had been shot, the Confederates with some one thousand horsemen fell on Sheridan's rear positions. Phil had anticipated such a possibility. His troopers, most of them dismounted, were behind breastworks, and crushed the assault, killing many Confederates, including Brigadier General James Gordon. It was the end of the Battle of Yellow Tavern.

Phil pushed on immediately and on May 12 had a fairly severe engagement with Confederate infantry and cavalry at Meadow Bridge, just north of Richmond. By clever use of artillery and cavalry, he beat back the onslaughts and he and his men proceeded in a leisurely

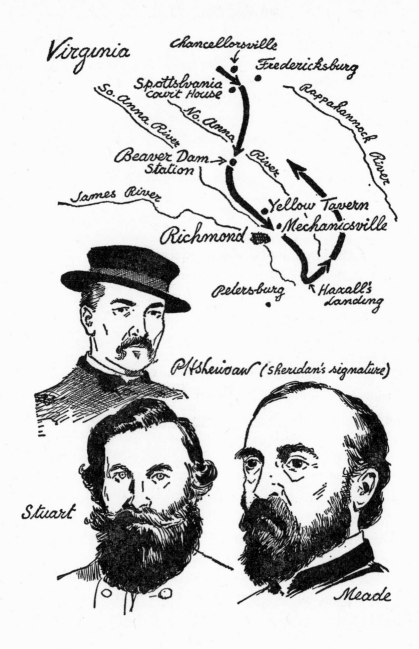

Virginia

Chancellorsville
Fredericksburg
Spottsylvania Court House
Rappahannock River
So. Anna River
No. Anna
Beaver Dam Station → River
James River
Yellow Tavern
Mechanicsville
Richmond
Petersburg
← Haxall's Landing

P H Sheridan (Sheridan's signature)

Stuart

Meade

way to Haxall's Landing on the James River, within Union lines. After a few days' rest the column swung north at Chesterfield and on May 24 made contact with Meade, whose forces had scored advances southward since Phil's departure.

During the advance east and southeast of Richmond, Phil had occasion to remember the pet theory of his one-time commander in the Northwest, Rains. The advance of his cavalry was bothered by crude land mines which killed a number of horses and men. Phil, in high anger, ordered Confederate prisoners to deactivate them. It was a dangerous job, but fortunately none of the Confederates was hurt.

The Richmond raid, as it is generally known, was a striking success and a big feather in Phil's hat. He realized later that his force could actually have taken Richmond with ease. At the time, however, he felt it would be taking a big chance and wring needless sacrifice from his troopers for no durable results. And Phil was not the man to throw his men into combat recklessly with personal glory in mind.

There was no long period of rest for Phil—not with Grant moving inexorably on Cold Harbor and Richmond. He was ordered to move south with two of his divisions ahead of Federal troops crossing the Pamunkey River, northeast of Richmond. The Rebels contested almost every mile of the advance.

The first sharp engagement occurred May 28 at Haw's Shop where Confederate cavalry, dismounted, had taken up positions behind breastworks, defending the road to Cold Harbor. The Southern Cavalry, which had been reinforced by M. C. Butler's brigade from South Carolina, was now organized in three divisions under Wade Hampton, Fitzhugh Lee and W. H. F. Lee, veterans who were not all in a class with the fabulous Stuart.

One attack by Gregg's division was blunted by the Confederates. Phil was determined to break through, however, and ordered Custer and his division to charge— all men dismounted. Custer, who did not relish walking when a horse was around, fumed somewhat at such a charge but had to obey. As a compensation, designed to add some glamor to this operation in swampy, humid thickets and trees, "Yellow Hair" ordered his band to play stirring tunes while they went into battle.

The Confederates were routed and Sheridan pushed on, entering Cold Harbor. On June 3 Grant launched his infantry against Lee's strong positions just west of Cold Harbor. It was an ill-stared frontal attack, the shortest and bloodiest combat experience of the Army of the Potomac. The attack lasted less than eight minutes. When it was over the Federals had suffered some six thousand casualties to fifteen hundred Confederate losses, and nothing had been achieved.

In June, Phil carried out another ambitious raid, against the town of Trevilian, a hub of the Virginia Central Railway, northwest of Richmond. On June 10 and 11 a stiff engagement occurred at Trevilian between the two Federal cavalry divisions used in this raid and Confederate horse, but nothing conclusive was achieved.

Sheridan decided to pull back in the face of increasingly powerful enemy forces, after damaging a considerable stretch of railway track. He was running very low on ammunition, his horses were exhausted and he had to convoy to comparative safety four hundred of his wounded, five hundred Confederate prisoners and two thousand Negro men, women and children. The Negroes had decided to liberate themselves and had simply attached themselves to the Federal column, which did the best it could for them.

"Probably not one of the poor things had the remotest idea, when they set out, as to where he would finally land, but to a man they followed the Yankees in full faith that they would lead them to freedom, no matter what road they took," Phil recalled.

The mixed column, suffering from intense heat, lack of food and water, not to mention medical attention, made its way back to the Federal zone north of Richmond. The Negroes, the prisoners and the wounded were routed under escort to West Point on the York River, while the rest of the command proceeded to White House Landing on the Pamunkey, northeast of Richmond.

In July Sheridan and his cavalry went into rest camp at Lighthouse Point to refit and recruit new men to replace the heavy casualties suffered in the Richmond and Trevilian raids and other operations. The cavalry corps had been in almost continuous action for nearly fifty days, and about fifteen hundred of its horses had been killed.

There were some gayer hours for Phil and his officers during this rest period, which would be brief. The wives of many officers came down to Grant's headquarters at City Point on the James River. There were balls and receptions which Phil attended in dress uniform, his garb, as usual, ill-fitting on his badly proportioned frame. During this time he met captivating Mrs. Custer. They took an immediate liking to each other and Phil even danced with her. She wrote friends that his dancing was "too funny" for words but added that he was "very bright" and a "jolly and agreeable" bachelor. She said she wished she could bring him to her home town of Monroe, Michigan, and marry him off to some attractive local maiden. They would remain good friends for many years. Sheridan always considered her a very special lady who exerted an excellent influence on her mercurial husband.

Major fighting continued everywhere while the cavalry was readied for action. The rest period ended in July. A man "worth his weight in gold" could not be kept long inactive. While there was dancing and merriment on the James, the Confederates were raising cain again in the Shenandoah Valley, one of the richest farmlands in the entire country and vital "breadbasket" of the Confederacy. At their head was the formidable

Confederate leader, bearded, angular, tall **Jubal A. Early.**

On August 1, 1864, Phil was detached from the Army of the Potomac to undertake an independent operation. The hardest and biggest battles of his meteoric career were imminent. He would sweep through the valley like an avenging storm, the tattoo of his black horse's hoofs re-echoing menacingly from the Alleghenies to the Blue Ridge Mountains. The climax of his military career was at hand.

CHAPTER **12**

"WE SENT THEM WHIRLING..."

On a sultry day in early August of 1864, a special train coming from Washington chugged into the railway station at Harpers Ferry on the Potomac River, at the northern end of the Blue Ridge Mountains.

When the train came to a stop, whistle blowing, brakes grinding, Phil Sheridan alighted, accompanied by a number of officers. After supervising the unloading of his black horse and giving it an affectionate pat on the neck, Sheridan and his escort proceeded to a nearby two-story building. Although his arrival went virtually unnoticed, he was a very important person indeed. He was to sweep the Shenandoah Valley of Jubal Early's

Confederates and give the entire area the "scorched earth" treatment so that it would be valueless to the enemy. His army grouped about forty-eight thousand men, infantry, cavalry, and artillery; his command was absolute, under Grant.

Sheridan settled down in the building in Harpers Ferry to plan his campaign.

"At Harpers Ferry I made my headquarters in the second story of a small and very dilapidated hotel," Phil wrote. "As soon as I was settled I sent for Lt. John R. Meigs . . . to study with him the maps of my geographical division. It always came rather easy to me to learn the geography of a new section and its important topographical features as well. Therefore I found that with the aid of Meigs, who was most intelligent in his profession, the region in which I was to operate would soon be well fixed in my mind."

Meigs was an invaluable man for Phil. A lieutenant in the engineers, he knew every twist of the Shenandoah landscape, down to remote farmhouses and little-known streams and roads. For several days Phil and Meigs pored over maps and discussed the terrain in general.

The Shenandoah, more officially known as the "Valley of Virginia," was a cemetery for Federal military reputations. Time and again Federal commanders had been bested in the valley. All could remember what happened to bewildered Unionists when the South's redoubtable Thomas "Stonewall" Jackson cut loose in the valley in 1862. Now Early was storming around the valley and beyond, sending shudders down official and other spines in Washington. On July 11 his army—numbering some twenty thousand infantry and cavalry—had reached a point close to the northern defenses of the capital city, cutting its telegraphic communications with the North and filling the city with despair.

Grant realized that so long as there was a Confederate army in the valley the communications of the Army of the Potomac, coiled in the Richmond-Cold Harbor area, would be unsafe. Early would have to be crushed quickly.

Sheridan had secured the transfer to his army of a number of officers who had been with his cavalry in the Army of the Potomac. They included Crook, Custer, Torbert and General Wesley Merritt. The latter had drawn Phil's attention by outstanding service in the Potomac Army and was now put in command of the First Cavalry Division of the Shenandoah force.

Phil's assignment was not easy. On paper his army consisted of about forty-eight thousand infantry, cavalry and artillerists. But of this number he could—according to his memoirs—only use about twenty-six thousand men as a striking force at the moment. Early's combat effectives were somewhere between seventeen and twenty thousand when Phil reached Harpers Ferry.

Besides being totally strange terrain to Phil, the valley was the "hunting ground" of the Confederate Colonel John S. Mosby and his guerrilla rangers. They were small in number but their sting could be vicious at any time. In fact, a fairly large sector of northern Virginia, just west of Washington, was ruefully referred to by

Shenandoah Mts

Harper's Ferry

Winchester
Berryville
Cedar Creek
Strasburg

Shenandoah Mts

Washington

Massanutten Mt

Shenandoah R.

Blue Ridge Mts

Virginia

Rapidan R

Rappahannock R.

Potomac R.

Early's drive north
from Lynchburg and Salem

Fredericksburg

Main theater
of operations

Washington
Richmond
Lynchburg

Early

Virginia

Early

Northerners as "Mosby's Confederacy." In addition, the majority of the natives were strongly pro-South.

Sheridan went into action immediately, but cautiously, pushing the Confederates back in minor engagements toward Cedar Creek, near Strasburg. All this was strictly preliminary sparring, for neither opponent sought a test of strength in August or the early part of September.

Learning in mid-August that Jubal Early had been reinforced by Lee with some six thousand infantry and cavalry, including the veteran Kershaw division, Sheridan pulled back to a strong defensive line at Halltown, near Harpers Ferry. Teamwork with his superior, Grant, was involved in this. Grant had urged him to fall back until Grant could launch some diversionary action near Richmond to force Lee to withdraw the reinforcements.

During the withdrawal, Phil, obeying instructions, unleashed total war. He ruthlessly destroyed supplies of grain and hay not needed by his army, by fire when necessary. In turn, the Confederates probed at various Federal positions but were effectively repulsed. It was clear that Sheridan was very much on the alert for any surprise. Nonetheless, Early formed the opinion that "this fellow Sheridan" was a cautious commander, a very serious misconception on his part.

Always keen on improving his information about the enemy, Phil, in early September, created a special mounted battalion of roving scouts, partly to keep tabs on Mosby but mainly to secure intelligence of any kind about Early's movements and convey it swiftly to headquarters. They were given permission to don Confederate uniforms when needed and would receive bonus pay from special Federal funds for valuable intelligence. Major H. K. Young of the First Rhode Island Infantry was placed in command, a hard-riding, resourceful officer who thoroughly relished this kind of work.

In a few days his questing men got on the track of something interesting and immediately reported the matter to Phil. Sheridan at that moment was particularly interested in rumors that the veteran Confederate Kershaw division had been withdrawn following a new threatening move by Grant in the Richmond area.

His horse rearing, wheeling and galloping, Phil stormed back and forth along the Berryville-Winchester road on the morning of September 19, 1864, roaring volleys of oaths of a violence seldom surpassed in the department of battle swearing. The cause—a traffic jam.

"Get those tarnation——wagons into the ditch," he shouted. "Come on, come on, you so-and-so's, move, move by——let's clear this road, let's get the infantry through."

His face was scarlet with rage as he sped up and down the line, shouting at the teamsters, threatening them with the flat of his sword as he warned them to make haste. He had good reason to be furious. The guns were already bellowing before Winchester; the battle was joined. And now his carefully-prepared tactical plan for the battle in which he was in top command was going awry.

The road from Berryville westward toward Winchester ran through a deep gorge for a distance of several miles west of Opequon Creek. Phil had ordered the bulk of his army to proceed along this road and fall into prearranged positions facing Early at Winchester. The 6th Corps under General Horatio Wright had passed through the gorge and had immediately come under heavy Confederate fire. But Wright had made one mistake. His train of ambulances, supply wagons, baggage and forage vehicles followed his infantry, clogging the road. Thousands of other troops scheduled to take up positions alongside Wright could not move forward through the ravine because of the traffic jam.

Sheridan, who was riding in the front with the 6th Corps, suddenly realized that something was wrong in his rear, threatening the smooth alignment of his central battle position. He sped back on Rienzi to take personal charge. The moment was one of the gravest in his career. Wright and his men were practically alone, facing the enemy. If the Confederates could shatter this corps and attack his army in the ravine and beyond, a military disaster was almost inevitable for the Army of the Shenandoah.

Phil did succeed by almost superhuman effort in having the road sufficiently cleared to permit passage of his other corps and formed his center. But the formation was behind schedule, being only completed in late morning. In later years he would always recall this morning as one of the tensest moments in his career.

The battle waged that day is usually referred to by Southern historians as the Third Battle of Winchester, in view of previous engagements in that area. Northern writers customarily call it the Battle of the Opequon, since this creek had to be crossed by the Army of the Shenandoah to reach Winchester. The South usually named major battles after the nearest town or center of population. The North whenever possible chose a familiar terrain feature such as a mountain, river, or creek for a battle name.

Somewhat troubled by Sheridan's relative inactivity, Grant had hurried north and conferred with Phil at Charleston on September 17, two days before the Battle of the Opequon. Northern morale had been given a shot in the arm earlier that month by news that Sherman had entered Atlanta, Georgia, but newspapers were still clamoring for action in the Shenandoah. Sherman had told Grant in previous weeks that Phil "would worry Early to death." Grant had no cause for anxiety. To him Phil outlined a bold offensive plan to bring Early to battle.

Sheridan spoke volubly but clearly. He planned to strike immediately. He had discovered that Early's force was spread in scattered formation near Martinsburg, west of Harpers Ferry, and southward toward Winchester, and he would try to attack the Confederates piecemeal.

Grant listened attentively. In his pocket were sheets

of paper on which he had outlined his own plan. Phil's was just as good, and Grant gave Phil an order which has gone down in history as a model of military brevity.

"Go in," was all that Grant said.

General fighting started about noontime. As soon as his troops were positioned, Phil launched a big attack with some twenty thousand men. The attack was progressing slowly under galling fire at great cost of life when Early spotted an opportunity. There was a gap between two of Sheridan's corps. The Confederates stormed forward with heavy artillery support and the Federal line bent and finally buckled. Phil's center was caving in. The fields on both sides of the Berryville pike were filled with panic-stricken Federals, wounded and unwounded, streaming toward the rear, yelling Confederates piling after them with fixed bayonets.

There was nothing to stop the Rebels except Battery E. Fifth Maine Light Artillery Regiment. The gunners did not panic, although they and their guns were a lone island in the midst of chaos. Heroically they poured volley after volley into the enemy, causing a slowdown in the assault.

Sheridan, riding on a knoll near the attack area, struck back. A brigade of the Federal 6th Corps fell on the flank of the Confederate assault column and forced it to withdraw in heavy fighting. Fleeing Union infantrymen were regrouped and the gap was filled.

Then Phil ordered able George Crook to bring his corps, which had been held in reserve, into full action, and Crook's batteries joined other artillery in battering the Confederates. Crook's infantry swept ahead in an attack against the Confederate left.

While this fighting forced the Rebels to form a new line closer to Winchester, Sheridan's cavalry, the tentacles of double envelopment which he had planned, were closing in on Early.

The cavalry under Wilson, which had swung in a wide circle since morning, appeared suddenly in massed formation on the Confederate right. Hard-pressed, Early believed all the Union cavalry was there and hurriedly dispatched his own cavalry in that direction along with artillery to prevent a flanking debacle.

As his center began to bend under Federal frontal assaults, Early was now horrified to see another great cloud of horsemen descending on his left wing, Torbert and Custer, swords waving, horses at full gallop, in the lead. They slashed into the Confederates like a tornado, the Rebel left collapsed and the whole line began to crumble, hit on the flanks, in front and in the rear. The attack by the northern wing drove a confused mass of stragglers into the main Confederate positions, increasing the disorder. By nightfall, the Confederates were in full flight, southward toward Strasburg along the Valley Pike.

The Confederates succeeded in getting away, but as one Rebel officer put it, "The sight was sad, humiliating and disgusting; I never had seen our men in such a panic before."

Jubilantly, Phil wired the War Department that night that he had sent "the enemy whirling through Winchester" and also informed Grant of the victory, stating that his troops had behaved superbly.

One hundred guns boomed in Washington in honor of the victory and congratulatory telegrams poured into Winchester from Washington and City Point, the latter Grant's headquarters. Grant said he considered the victory "most opportune in time and effect . . . it wipes out much of the stain upon our arms by previous disasters in that vicinity."

"Have just heard of your great victory," Lincoln wired. "God bless you all, officers and men. Strongly inclined to come up and see you."

There was no time for Phil to savor congratulatory telegrams. He had promised to pursue the enemy "to the death." Early's army had not been destroyed. Federal cavalry patrols shadowing the retreat reported the Confederates were regrouping near Strasburg, concentrating near Fisher's Hill.

On September 20, at dawn, the army was on the move toward Fisher's Hill. The bitter fighting was by no means over. There would be victory followed by surprise and near-disaster. Phil's greatest ride on Rienzi was in the offing, to be immortalized in stirring poetry by James Buchanan Read.

CHAPTER **13**

FORWARD EVERYTHING!

On the night of September 20, Phil Sheridan, George Crook, and other officers of his army pored over a field map in the commander's campaign tent.

An oil lamp cast a flickering light on the bronzed, lean faces and into the dim tent shadows. Outside, the trees rustled in a night breeze, the sound punctuated by the voices of soldiers hunkered before their bivouac fires and the occasional snort or shuffling of a horse. Toward the south, beyond the tent and the fires, rose the wooded, mysterious heights of Little North Mountain and Massanutten Mountain. Between these two

143

mountains flickered other bivouac fires, kindled by troops of "Old Jube" Early.

His right flank now rested on the Massanutten Mountain and the north fork of the Shenandoah River. His left stretched toward Little North Mountain with its steep and thickly-wooded slopes, now dark in the night. His infantry was entrenched on Fisher's Hill, a steep bluff overhanging the south bank of Tumbling Run Creek. Nearby, just north of the Shenandoah, lay the little town of Strasburg. The Confederate line was about four miles long, defended by some twelve to thirteen thousand troops. Detachments of Southern cavalry had been swung beyond Massanutten Mountain to check a possible enemy left flanking movement through the Luray Valley.

Sheridan on this night had cause for personal gratification over the Opequon Creek battle. A major general of volunteers, he had been promptly promoted by the War Department to Brigadier General in the Regular Army. Nonetheless, Phil was not satisfied with the results of the victory. Early had not really been knocked out.

The classic double envelopment was again on Phil's mind as he stroked his chin and gazed reflectively at the map. He and his officers had closely studied the enemy position through field glasses during the daylight hours. All realized that it was a tough nut to crack, although Federal effectives were far greater in number.

"As you know, gentlemen," Phil said, "I am sending most of my cavalry on a wide swing through the Luray

Valley, to circle Massanutten Mountain and come up in the rear of the enemy's right flank. Sixth and 19th Corps will move frontally. Any major attack here will depend on flank developments. I favor at this point a hard blow against the Rebel right by the Eighth Corps. Any questions? Yes, George. . . ."

George Crook, who commanded the Eighth, looked worried, and his expression had caught Phil's eye.

"You know, Phil, I'll do anything you say," Crook said. "But I do respectfully object. They're very strong there at the base of Massanutten. May I suggest that my corps move against their left. There I could work surprise and we could use that. It is heavily wooded and my men know how to march silently."

For several minutes Phil pondered Crook's suggestion, studying the map. Then he raised his head and said:

"George, you may be right at that. We'll do that. Fine, go in. By heaven, we may have an Indian trick for 'Old Jubilee!' Play 'possum in this forest," Phil pointed to a spot north of Strasburg on the map, "until tomorrow night. Move out in darkness and keep your boys quiet. That will be all for tonight, gentlemen."

The whole battle plan for Fisher's Hill depended on keeping Crook's movements secret. The enemy had a signal station called Three Top on a high elevation which could easily spot any major daylight troop movements.

The Eighth Corps lay concealed in the designated forest all of September 21. When darkness fell, Crook

145

and his men, some seven thousand warriors, snaked out of the forest and headed for Little North Mountain by a circuitous route.

Crook, who one day would become a noted Indian fighter, took no chances regarding detection. Weapons were wrapped in rags to prevent glints of light of any kind; striking matches for any purpose was forbidden, and the men were ordered to adorn their hats with leafy branches. No loud talking; no bivouac fires. Even the color-bearers trailed their flags.

Meanwhile, Sheridan had brought the Sixth and 19th Corps under Wright and Emory into frontal alignment about eight hundred yards from the Confederate line, which had been strengthened by rifle pits and trenches. Skirmishing had occurred on Early's front as the Federals took over some minor hillocks, but there was nothing to indicate that Phil intended any massive frontal assault.

Confident that their position was impregnable, the Confederates little dreamed what lurked on the slopes to their left. Cook fires already were being lit in their lines at sundown on September 22 when pickets reported they had seen Union troops moving along the steep slopes of Little North Mountain. A Rebel battery opened up against them, but it was too late.

With whirlwind suddenness the Rebel left was struck in flank and rear. Crook's West Virginians advanced to their own battle cry, an eerie sound which, according to Crook, was most unnerving and "beggared description."

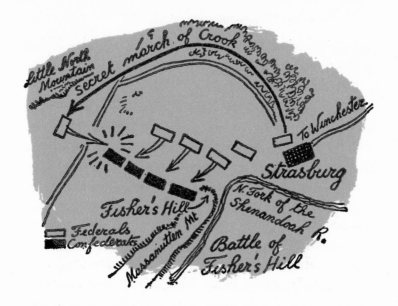

While artillery thundered on both sides, one of Wright's divisions on the Federal right swung into action to catch the Rebel left in a vise. Almost simultaneously, all the Federals in the front streamed forward, Sheridan on Rienzi, waving his black plug hat, in the forefront.

"Forward everything! Don't stop! Go on, on!" Phil shouted.

Caught in this frontal and left flank storm, the entire Confederate position collapsed and Early's men fled southward in "indescribable confusion." Only stiff rearguard action and the approach of night saved them from total annihilation.

It was a decisive victory and Union casualties were comparatively light, totaling some 528 men, 52 of them killed in action. The Confederates admitted a loss of 1,235 men, probably an underestimation. Sixteen Confederate guns were captured.

For Phil, however, there was one bitter pill. The big mass of cavalry he had sent into the Luray Valley in a left flank swipe, although led by trusted commanders, had moved sluggishly. It failed to pierce Confederate cavalry guarding the road to the south. If this had been done, Early would have been in a bag and his force wiped out or forced to surrender.

"Astonished and chagrined," Phil without more ado sacked veteran divisional cavalry commander W. W. Averill and replaced him with another officer. Torbert, who was in top command in this thrust, was not relieved, but Phil was deeply disappointed in him in this instance.

The pursuit of Early continued southward until September 26, but wily Jube remained one jump ahead and reached the vicinity of Port Republic, far south in the valley.

The "scorched earth" which had seared large sections in the northern areas now was applied to the southern area, which had scarcely felt the conqueror's fist since the war began. Phil was ruthless in obeying orders, although the task was distasteful to him. Barns and stables were destroyed, crops ruined and cattle driven off. The breadbasket of the Army of Northern Virginia was now a vale of desolation.

The work of destruction completed, Phil moved his

army into position along Cedar Creek, close to Strasburg and some twenty miles south of Winchester, on October 10.

Phil was on the alert for trouble. Reports had come in that indomitable Jubal Early had been heavily reinforced. Determined to check Sheridan's campaign, Lee had sent the picked Kershaw division, withdrawn in the previous month, and a whole brigade of cavalry to Early. He now had 18,400 men in his command and was on the move to strike another blow. On October 13, he appeared in force around the very same Fisher's Hill where he had been beaten in September.

Sheridan's army was concentrated on the north side of Cedar Creek, astride the Valley Pike just south of Middletown. The position, crowning a line of low hills, was well chosen to block any Confederate move northward along the Pike.

It had one serious weakness. On the Union left, held by Crook and his Eighth Corps, lay a good mile of unprotected open ground extending to the junction of Cedar Creek and the north fork of the Shenandoah River.

There was a deep, seemingly impassable gorge where creek and river joined, close to the nose of Massanutten Mountain. The possibility that an attack might come over the rugged, wooded nose of the Massanutten and then through the gorge, smashing against the Federal left and its rear, had been discounted. Crook was in a particularly dangerous position, but did not realize it.

He would soon be the target of a secret Indian-style attack closely resembling that which he carried out at Fisher's Hill.

At this critical moment, questions of higher strategy entered the picture. On October 13, much to his annoyance, Phil received a telegram from War Secretary Stanton to proceed to Washington for a few days. The purpose was to discuss future movements of the Army of the Shenandoah and coordination of this army's movements with Grant's pressure on Petersburg and Richmond. The order could not be ignored.

Appointing General Wright temporary commander, Phil boarded a train for Washington on October 16 at Port Royal, accompanied by his brother and other members of his personal staff.

Phil had excellent intuition—almost infallible. He was gnawed by worry with good reason. In a few days the victorious Army of the Shenandoah would face the darkest moment of the entire campaign. And Phil would be miles away.

CHAPTER **14**

"THE DAMNDEST TWIST"

At about 10 P.M., Phil Sheridan, his faced lined with
fatigue, said goodnight to various officers with whom he
had been conferring and went upstairs to his bed-
chamber in the Logan house in Winchester. It was the
night of October 18, 1864.

He still felt the strain of hour-long talks with "Old
Brains" Halleck and Stanton in Washington on the
previous day. It was only after considerable discussion
that he had convinced them that his plan of operations
for the Army of the Shenandoah was the best. Grant
favored a further advance through the Blue Ridge
Mountains toward Richmond and Petersburg. Phil ad-

vocated establishment of a strong holding defense line in the Shenandoah and eventual shipment of the bulk of his army by rail via Washington to the Petersburg-Richmond zone. Stanton and Halleck finally had come around to Phil's point of view.

Anxious over the situation of his forces at Cedar Creek, Phil, even before the conference began, had asked the War Department to keep a special train in readiness for him in the capital. Immediately after the close of the talks, Phil and his staff hurried to the railway station and boarded the train bound for Martinsburg, west of Harpers Ferry. Rienzi and the other horses had already been placed in freight cars in the train during the morning.

After a short night's rest at Martinsburg, Sheridan mounted Rienzi and, accompanied by his staff and a cavalry escort, reached Winchester late in the afternoon of the 18th. The cavalcade should have made Winchester much earlier; the distance was only twenty-eight miles. But two engineer colonels, named Alexander and Thom, had been attached to the Sheridan party by the War Department to survey terrain for possible defense lines. Alexander was enormously fat and Thom very thin. Both were very poor horsemen, and out of courtesy to them the cavalcade maintained a slower pace than was desired. Everybody should have been galloping, in view of what was brewing in the minds of Early and his officers.

"As soon as we arrived at Colonel Edwards' house (the Logan residence)—where I intended stopping for

the night—I sent a courier to the front to bring me a
report of the situation," Phil wrote in his memoirs.
"Then I took Colonel Alexander on a survey of the
heights around Winchester. . . . By the time we had
completed our survey it was dark. Just as we reached
Colonel Edwards' house on our return a courier came
in from Cedar Creek bringing word that everything was
all right, that the enemy was quiet at Fisher's Hill and
that a brigade of Grover's division was to make a reconnaissance in the morning, the 19th. About 10 o'clock I
went to bed greatly relieved and expecting to rejoin my
headquarters at my leisure next day."

All was not quiet at Cedar Creek. As Phil slept,
shadowy figures were scrambling up and down wooded
slopes and rocky ledges near the junction of Cedar Creek
and the Shenandoah. Shortly after midnight Custer's
Officer of the Day making his rounds heard a noise in
a wooded area beyond the Federal pickets. Believing the
noise was being made by some Union cavalryman, he
entered the trees to investigate. Suddenly dark shapes
rushed him, and before he could make an outcry he was
knocked down and made prisoner. A number of sentries,
half-asleep in the morning fog, were similarly dealt with
on the fringe of the Federal left flank.

While Phil was heading back to Winchester from
Washington, the Confederates had evolved an excellent
battle plan, its keynote surprise, always an important
factor in military success. They obtained a splendid
view of the entire Federal position from the lofty Three
Top signal station on Massanutten Mountain. They

noticed that Crook's Eighth Corps was somewhat detached from the remainder of the Federal forces. It was open for a smashing right hook if troops could attack through the gorge. Confederate scouts discovered that there was a little-known path that led through the defile to two fords of the Shenandoah, about one and one-half miles from Crook's position.

Brigadier General John B. Gordon, one of Early's finest commanders, reportedly suggested a secret march with some of the best troops through the gorge area. Early approved and placed Gordon in command of this column. Simultaneously, Early would advance along the Valley Turnpike through Strasburg with the remainder of his force—infantry, including the Kershaw division, artillery and cavalry—and strike at the Federals in a coordinated attack. The entire Rebel plan was aided by the fact that Phil's temporary commander in the area, Wright, was principally worried about his right flank, not his left. Crook's corps was in reality only of divisional strength at this time, some five thousand men, and the Confederates were aware of it. The usually vigilant Crook had somehow been lulled into a sense of security. His reconnaissance was sketchy, and pickets were stationed too close to his encampment.

Before midnight, October 18, the Southern force was on the move, in two main wings; watches were coordinated for combined attacks at 5 A.M. of the following day.

In single file, like Indians, Gordon's three divisions moved stealthily along the chosen path and reached jumping off positions after crossing the two fords of the Shenandoah. General Gordon has left a graphic description of the latter phase of his secret march.

"For nearly an hour we waited for the appointed time, resting near the bank of the river. . . . Everything conspired to make conditions both thrilling and weird. The men were resting, lying in long lines on the thickly-matted grass or reclining in groups, their hearts thumping, their ears eagerly listening for the orders: 'Attention, men! Fall in! Forward!' In the still, starlit night the only sounds heard were the gentle rustle of leaves in the October wind, the low murmur of the Shenandoah flowing swiftly along its rocky bed and dashing against the limestone cliffs that bordered it . . . the subdued tones or half-whispers of men as they thoughtfully communed with each other as to the fate which might befall each in the next hour. . . ."

Phil Sheridan was asleep when the Confederates hit his army like a thunderclap. Early, his artillery booming, struck frontally at Crook, and Gordon's veterans attacked from the rear.

Phil Sheridan was awakened at 6 A.M. in Winchester. By that time the Cedar Creek situation was catastrophic. The surprise was complete. Crook's corps disintegrated first, and then W. H. Emory's 19th Corps broke and fled. Only Wright's Sixth Corps and scattered regiments from other units held their ground in a desperate position on the Federal right. Everything else was in panicky flight northward through Middletown toward Winchester.

Sheridan was still in bed in the Logan house when an officer on duty reported at his bedside that artillery fire could be heard coming from Cedar Creek.

"Is the fire continuous?" Sheridan asked.

"Irregular and fitful, sir," the officer replied.

"Oh, it's all right, it's probably Grover who has gone out on reconnaissance and is feeling the enemy," Phil replied with a yawn.

Phil turned over in bed to get some more sleep. Fortunately for the Army of the Shenandoah and the Union cause, a warning bell clanged in his brain.

"I grew so restless that I could not sleep and soon got up and dressed myself," he recalled in his memoirs. "A little later the picket officer came back and reported that the firing, which could be distinctly heard from his line on the heights outside Winchester, was still going on. I asked him if it sounded like a battle and as he again said that it did not, I still inferred that the cannonading was caused by Grover's division. . . .

"However, I went downstairs and requested that breakfast be hurried up and at the same time ordered the horses to be saddled for I had decided to go to the front. . . ."

Shortly before 9 A.M. Phil mounted Rienzi, the big black in fine morning fettle, head tossing, eyes flashing, legs restive, tail twitching. Escorted by personal staff officers also on horseback and a cavalry detachment, the cavalcade headed southward through Winchester at a brisk trot. The morning fog had lifted and a bright autumn sun shone down from a cloudless sky on the russet hills and valleys of beautiful northern Virginia.

As they trotted along, Sheridan became increasingly convinced that the Union Army must be in trouble. The cavalcade crossed Mill Creek south of Winchester and ascended a low, sloping hill. Beyond the hill was a nightmare sight for any commander.

"There burst upon our view the appalling spectacle of a panic-stricken army—hundreds of slightly wounded men, throngs of others unhurt but utterly demoralized and baggage wagons by the score, all pressing to the rear in hopeless confusion, telling only too plainly that disaster had occurred at the front. . . ."

Fugitives who had not been wounded told Phil that the battle was lost, the army completely routed. Phil disregarded this and immediately instructed Colonel Edwards in Winchester to post his brigade across Mill Creek and check the flight.

Phil decided to get to the battle front wherever it was in the Cedar Creek area. Ordering twenty men, including two staff officers, to follow him, he headed southward. As he dashed up the pike the crowds of stragglers grew thicker.

"Swinging his cap with a cheery smile for all, he shouted 'Face the other way, boys! Face the other way! We're going back to our camps, all of us! We are going to lick them out of their boots!' " the noted newspaperman, Whitelaw Reid, wrote in his account of the ride in his book *Ohio in the War.*

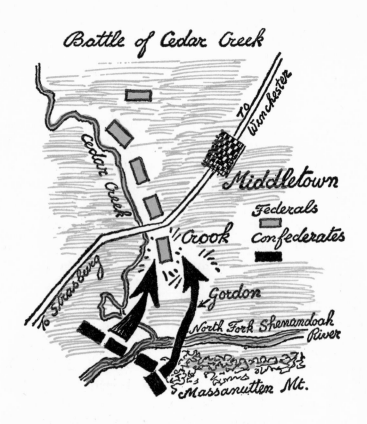

The wounded raised their hoarse voices to cheer him as he passed with shouts of "Here comes Little Phil! Phil is back! Phil is back!"

First to one group, then to another, Phil shouted:

"Boys, this never should have happened if I had been here. I tell you it never should have happened. We're going back, we'll get the damndest twist on them you ever saw. We'll have all those cannons back again."

Many stragglers had coolly settled down in the fields to boil coffee, but when they saw Phil they cheered,

"Face the other way, boys!"

seized their weapons, and began following him. By twos, by threes, by dozens, by hundreds, the discouraged and the beaten took heart as if the "forked lightning" had electrified them with fresh courage. In swelling numbers they began the road back.

"The first thing that attracted my attention was the clatter of horses' feet on the pike and the most vociferous cheering I ever heard," a Vermont private who was in the retreat reported. "When I looked up I saw General Sheridan coming, followed by his bodyguard. Sheridan was about fifty yards in advance with his hat in his hand, shouting as near as I could understand 'come to the front with me, boys, and we will make this matter all right.' It was an awful moment, but I could not help thinking of Jack the Giant Killer. But everybody and everything followed Sheridan. . . ."

Along the way an infantry colonel, suffering from bad combat shock, shouted wildly to Phil: "The army is whipped, whipped!"

"You are, but the army isn't," Phil shouted as he flashed by.

At Newtown, about seven miles north of Cedar Creek, the streets were so crowded with troops, many of them lacking half their clothes, horses, wagons and caissons, that Phil had to ride around the village. Here an officer galloped up and gave him his first direct news of the disastrous withdrawal of the Federal left and center. The officer, William McKinley of Crook's staff— McKinley the Ohioan who would become president in 1896—had some good news for Phil. Some troops, notably George Getty's division of the Sixth Corps and Merritt's and Custer's cavalry, were still in line.

As Sheridan neared the battle zone, there was a crescendo of shouting behind him as thousands of men came up in his wake, many of them capering, laughing, waving their muskets defiantly and throwing their caps in the air.

"With foam and with dust the black charger was
    gray;
By the flash of his eye, and his red nostrils' play,
He seemed to the whole great army to say,
I have brought Sheridan all the way
From Winchester, down to save the day."

Battered by the surprise onslaught, the troops of Getty and the Custer-Merritt horsemen had been pushed back in fierce fighting to positions just north of Middletown.

Phil arrived on the field about 10:30 A.M. The hard-pressed officers and men, who had felt that their doom was sealed, went wild with delight. Custer rode up to Phil and, leaning sideways in the saddle, threw his arms around his neck and kissed him on the cheek in full view of the cheering troopers.

Immediately, Phil took over command, reorganizing shattered divisions and regiments and re-forming bands of stragglers into new groupings. The Confederate command had halted its offensive by the time Phil arrived on the field. The assault troops were weary from night marching and fighting and needed regrouping.

Early assertedly hesitated about launching an all-out attack on what remained of the Federal line, partly because of the Custer-Merritt cavalry threat. Perhaps he felt that victory already had been won. He rejected insistent proposals by Gordon that a final attack be made in the morning. This gave Phil much-needed time at a very crucial moment.

At 3 P.M. Early Confederates launched an attack against one section of the Federal line, but it was easily beaten back. Then Phil gave the signal at 4 P.M., and the whole Federal line, including cavalry, swept forward like a blue tide. Phil, in the forefront, was mounted on a gray horse. He had perceived shortly before the attack that his black gelding was tired from the day's work and had sent him back to the rear to browse and rest.

The Confederates, protected by a stone fence and impromptu breastworks, were in a favorable position and put up very determined resistance. The Confederates counter-attacked against the flank of the 19th Corps, but this onslaught was hurled back and the Federal wave moved onward, its infantrymen attacking with "screams of delight and triumph."

Then Phil sent Custer's whole division in a thunderous charge against the enemy line, the horsemen making "the air tremble" with cheers as they galloped past Phil.

The Confederates were swept back against Cedar Creek, and in the confusion of attempting to cross it under severe fire, their withdrawal turned into panic and rout.

Phil was everywhere, his gray wheeling, galloping and rearing back on its haunches in sudden halts.

"Run! Go after them, get those bayonets into those those——!" he shouted whenever he spotted troops that were moving slowly.

When a battle-weary private gasped, "We can't run—we're all tuckered out," Phil yelled:

"If you can't run, then shoot and holler. We've got a twist on them, the damndest twist you ever saw!"

By dusk the field was cleared; the Southerners were driven back to Fisher's Hill and beyond, harried by Federal cavalry and infantry. The Confederate defeat in the valley was final. Early had lost most of his artillery, twenty-five guns, and some two dozen guns captured from the Federals, all his ambulances and ammunition wagons and most of his baggage and forage wagons. His casualties had been twenty-nine hundred, including some of his best officers. The Federals had suffered five thousand casualties in killed, wounded and missing.

Guns thundered in jubilation in Washington and elsewhere, and worry lines deepened in the face of Robert E. Lee. One more pillar in the archaic state known as the Confederacy had crashed in the battle smoke. In the Shenandoah "Little Phil" had dealt another shattering blow to an out-dated, tyrannical dream based on what was genteely referred to by the South as "the peculiar institution" of slavery.

President Lincoln sent a telegram to Phil lauding the deeds of him and his army in the name of the nation and expressing his own personal admiration "especially for the splendid work of October 19, 1864."

The one-time Herr Dresbach had fought his greatest and most theatrical battle, and on October 23 he was appointed a Major General in the Regular Army, the best news of his military career up to that time.

Sheridan's army settled down in winter quarters around Kernstown after the Battle of Cedar Creek. The winter months of 1864 and January, 1865, were generally quiet except for action against Mosby and other guerrillas and scouting operations shadowing Early, whose force was far down in the valley near Staunton.

In early February, 1865, Sheridan moved southward through the valley with two cavalry divisions, en route to join Grant in the Petersburg-Richmond area. At Waynesboro he gave the *coup-de-grace* to Early and his shadow of an army. The ill-starred Early, who had fought gallantly against heavy odds, fled to Petersburg. He was rewarded for his services by being relieved of command and sent home to await further orders. They never came.

Having placed General Winfield Hancock in command of the remainder of his Army in the Shenandoah, Sheridan and his cavalry joined up with Grant at White House Landing after a wearisome march over rainswept country.

More fighting was in the offing for Phil in 1865. He would be the nemesis of Robert E. Lee, a terrible Union bludgeon on the road to Appomattox.

CHAPTER **15**

GALLOPING NEMESIS

The arrival of colorful Phil Sheridan was an electrifying tonic for the siege-weary troops of Grant before Petersburg and Richmond.

The long drawn out and seemingly futile siege operations aimed at pushing Lee out of his fortifications complex had reduced the morale of the Army of the Potomac to its lowest pitch in months. The soldiers, plagued by malaria and swamp fever, were heartily sick of abortive attacks and monotonous sapping and digging operations, mud, rain and daily discomfort. Not only the dispirited troops but their commanders as well, from

Grant on down, viewed impending spring operations with a sense of dread rather than enthusiasm.

Wherever he appeared on horseback or afoot, Sheridan was loudly cheered and his democratic ways endeared him to every private and officer. His exploits in the Shenandoah and elsewhere were discussed with relish around evening campfires in the open or in bomb shelters.

"The personality of the man, not less than his renown, affected people," a reporter of the New York *Herald*, who was with Grant's armies, remarked. "A very Punch of soldiers, a sort of Rip van Winkle in regimentals, it astonished folks that with so jolly and grotesque a guise, he held within him energies like lightning, the bolts of which had splintered the fairest parts of the border."

Phil immediately became involved in complex dickering with Grant as to just where he should go and what he and his cavalrymen should do. Grant wanted Phil to link up with Sherman in the Carolinas and move against Joseph Johnston. Phil did not favor this idea at all. He felt he could be of far greater help to Grant in final drives to crush Lee in the Richmond-Petersburg area.

"I tell you I'm ready to strike out and smash them now! Let me go!" Major General Sheridan told Grant at a conference.

He believed that once he got in Lee's rear, smashed railroads supplying the besieged Confederates and forced the Rebels to come out fighting in the open the Confederacy's doom was sealed.

After considerable deliberation, Grant decided that Phil should operate with his armies and accorded him the title of "Commander-in-Chief of the Army of the Shenandoah, serving with the Army of the Potomac." It was agreed that Phil would make a big swing west and northwest of Petersburg, striking at Lee's right flank, roughly the area west of Petersburg. This would also threaten the Southside Railway, Lee's main supply artery. Two infantry corps, one of them commanded by Gouverneur Warren, one of the heroes of Gettysburg, would go into action simultaneously, ordered to support Phil when he deemed it necessary.

Early in the morning of March 29, a dreary, overcast day, Sheridan on Rienzi, his guidon-bearer behind him, rode out of Hancock Station, near Petersburg, and headed for Dinwiddie Courthouse. With him went some of his veteran commanders, including dependable George Crook, dashing Custer, and young but experienced Merritt. In their wake came some twelve thousand cavalrymen in three divisions, backed by powerful horse artillery. Every trooper was equipped with a repeating carbine. The combined firepower of Phil's army was vastly superior to anything Lee could throw against it. The first phase of the march was at a walk, which the troopers knew always foreshadowed hard fighting ahead.

"Our general direction was westward, over such

167

routes as we could find," Phil wrote. "The roads were in a frightful state from winter's frosts and rains. When it was sought to avoid a spot which the head of the column had proved almost bottomless, the bogs and quicksands of the adjoining fields demonstrated that to make a detour was to go from bad to worse. We floundered on, however, crossing on the way a series of small streams swollen to their banks. . . ."

On the first day's march, the cavalry seized and occupied Dinwiddie Courthouse, overcoming slight opposition.

"Lee at once recognized the danger, not only to the positions in Richmond and Petersburg, but also to his planned movement eventually to join up with Johnston (in the Carolina area)," the *Compact History of the Civil War* says in an excellent analysis of the situation at that moment.

"He reacted with typical vigor. He would attack, even though this still further reduced the strength in his thinly held fortifications. While A. P. Hill delayed the advance of Warren's corps and Humphrey (General Andrew Humphrey, commanding the Second Federal Corps) south of White Oak Road, Lee sent (General George) Pickett with two divisions and Fitzhugh Lee's cavalry—about 11,000 men in all—circling well to the west to strike the left flank of the advancing Federal columns.

"On March 31, the Confederates attacked. A. P. Hill drove around Warren's left flank and though eventually repulsed he succeeded in halting the Union infantry advance. At the same time Pickett struck Sheridan's cavalry northwest of Dinwiddie Courthouse. The fighting was hard and furious, but Sheridan would not give way even though faced by a force considerably larger than his own and consisting mostly of veteran infantry."

Pickett, whose name always will be associated with the famous infantry charge at Gettysburg, hurled his veterans against Sheridan at sundown. He had struck shrewdly. A considerable number of Phil's men were out on reconnaissance at that time and Pickett had numerical superiority. However, Sheridan's men at Dinwiddie Courthouse, most of them dismounted and entrenched, met the Confederates with such withering fire that "nothing could stand against it."

Pickett withdrew to nearby woods leaving hundreds of dead and dying on the field.

Phil's quick brain immediately realized that Pickett was isolated from the rest of the Confederate army and open to a devastating counterstroke. He immediately appealed to Grant to place an infantry corps under his orders for a combined offensive against Pickett. Warren's Fifth Corps, on Grant's order, was assigned to Phil and ordered to join him that very night. Simultaneously, Sheridan sent Warren orders to attack Pickett's rear at dawn, April 1.

Pickett, however, had received word of the approach of Union infantry and pulled back during the night to

169

Five Forks, just south of the Southside Railway. Here he entrenched, obeying telegraphed instructions from Lee to "hold Five Forks at all hazards."

Sheridan and his men moved up fast after Pickett. Phil ordered Warren also to advance rapidly and hit Pickett's left flank while the cavalrymen, on foot, pinned down the enemy in frontal demonstrations.

Warren moved somewhat slowly, however, and his troops did not go into action until late in the afternoon of April 1, when Phil's men already were exchanging fire with Pickett's men.

Sheridan, who was angered by Warren's lateness, immediately ordered an all-out assault. A Confederate counter-attack staggered part of Warren's infantry. The Federals were on the verge of confusion when Sheridan galloped up to the crucial sector.

"Where is my battle flag?" he shouted.

A cavalry sergeant spurred up to him with the swallow-tailed flag. Sheridan grabbed it and ordered the infantry forward again, "dashing from one point of the line to another waving his flag, shaking his fist, encouraging, threatening, praying, swearing, the very incarnation of battle," according to one eyewitness.

On the left and on the right the Federals stormed forward and nothing could stop them. Phil led the decisive charge himself, brandishing his flag, and finally jumping his big black over the Confederate breastworks.

Somewhat carelessly, Pickett had gone to a point well behind the line to attend a shadbake tendered by one of the Confederate officers. Hearing the swelling noise of guns and muskets, he rushed back. It was too late; his defense line had crumbled and his troops were melting away in panic. About 6,000 Confederates were taken prisoner. Pickett escaped, but his force—one of Lee's best—was irretrievably shattered. The Union loss was 634 killed and wounded. There is no record of Southern casualties. Six guns and 13 battle flags also were seized by the Federals.

As the battle ended, a Rebel who had surrendered shouted to Phil: "Where do you want us all to go?"

"Go right over there," Phil shouted jovially. "Go right over there. Drop your guns; you'll never need them any more. You'll be safe over there. Are there any more of you? We want every one of you fellows."

Five Forks was the Waterloo of the Confederacy, in the view of many historians. Lee could do nothing now but withdraw from Petersburg, abandon Richmond and head west with dim hope that he could eventually move southwest and join up with Johnston farther south.

Immediately after the victory, Phil relieved Warren of his command, angered by what he felt were his dilatory tactics at a vital moment. Removing the hero of Little Round Top at Gettysburg from his command stirred up a controversy which was the subject of sharp arguing for decades following the war.

Then Phil and his horsemen and infantry pushed north toward the Southside Railway. He would be like a raging cougar in Lee's path.

Receiving the report of Sheridan's overwhelming victory at Five Forks, Grant ordered a general assault against Petersburg on the following morning. In massive dawn assaults, Federal troops broke through the main Confederate positions.

It was obvious to Lee on that gray, overcast Sunday that Richmond and Petersburg could no longer be defended. He sent a telegram to President Jefferson Davis in Richmond informing him of the decision. The President had his clerks burn official documents in the Confederate capital before he left by special train for Lynchburg and Danville, his flight shielded by Lee's withdrawing troops.

Lee's last ditch attempt to escape westward with his remaining forty thousand men was a tragic march, foredoomed to failure. His men fought hard and valiantly but the Federals were now in full cry in overwhelmingly superior numbers.

At Sailor's Creek, about fifty miles west of Petersburg, Phil dealt another smashing blow to Lee on April 6. After savage fighting, seven thousand Confederates surrendered, and two thousand fled through the woods to the Appomattox River, to be rounded up by Federal cavalry before nightfall. Six generals were captured, including the noted James B. Kershaw, R. S. Ewell, and Curtis Lee, son of the Southern Commander-in-Chief.

The Confederate "forlorn hope" came to an end on Palm Sunday, April 9, 1865, when Sheridan and his cavalry and a whole corps of infantry took up positions

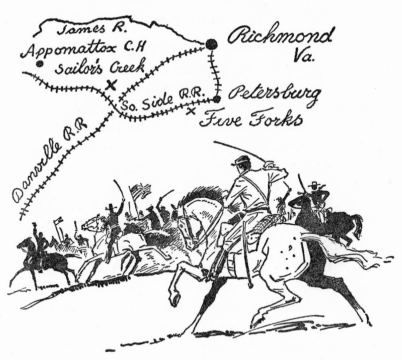

near Appomattox Court House. Lee could not advance any further. There were Yankees to his front, in the rear and on his flank in overwhelmingly superior numbers. There was some sharp fighting as the Confederates probed the Federal lines to see if they could be broken. They held firm. The firing died down, and Lee sent a courier with a white flag through the lines carrying a letter to Grant.

That day Lee signed surrender papers involving himself and the Army of Northern Virginia—28,356 officers and men. Phil was present at the surrender talks in the McLean House at Appomattox Court House. On this occasion he wore the full uniform of his rank, with sash, belt and saber.

While heading back to Petersburg with his cavalry, Phil heard the staggering news that President Lincoln had been shot by John Wilkes Booth in the Ford Theater in Washington and died on April 15.

In his memoirs, Phil recounts a strange episode. During the latter phase of the Shenandoah campaign, in February, a man named Lomas offered his services as a spy and was accepted. War Secretary Stanton had used him as an undercover agent and had recommended him. Shortly thereafter Lomas urged Phil to similarly employ another man who, he said, had served with Mosby but left him following a quarrel.

The man appeared before Phil completely disguised. On discarding his disguise "he proved to be a rather slender, dark-complexioned handsome young man . . . of captivating manners, who gave his name as Renfrew." Phil became convinced they were enemy agents and had them arrested and sent to Baltimore. There they escaped their guards and Phil never saw them again.

"I learned that after the assassination of President Lincoln, Secretary Stanton strongly suspected his friend Lomas of being associated with the conspirators and it then occurred to me that the good-looking Renfrew may have been Wilkes Booth for he certainly bore a strong resemblance to Booth's pictures."

CHAPTER **16**

"EYES RIGHT"

Major General Sheridan was fretful as he paced back and forth or sat in one of the big armchairs of his room in the Willard Hotel in Washington on Sunday, May 21, 1865.

Phil and most of his officers had arrived in Washington from the Petersburg area early that month and had been treated as celebrities by capital society. Phil had thoroughly enjoyed himself, tossing off bumpers of champagne with the best, savoring fine food, chatting with socially prominent men and women. His fretfulness was not a result of fatigue born of the "social whirl." It was caused by a pressing assignment from

Grant and the impending Grand Review of Union
Soldiers scheduled for May 23 and 24.

The day after his arrival in Washington he had been
notified by Grant that he had been relieved of command of the Middle Military Division and assigned to
command west of the Mississippi. "Your duty is to
restore Texas and that part of Louisiana held by the
enemy (rebellious Confederate General E. Kirby Smith
and his debilitated Army of the Trans-Mississippi) to
the Union in the shortest practicable time, in a way
most effectual for securing permanent peace," the order
said in part.

Phil promptly asked Grant, who was also in Washington, if he could leave after the Grand Review. He
longed to lead his cavalry corps when it would parade
in the review on the 24th. The answer was no. He must
leave by May 22nd at the latest.

Obeying orders, he completed arrangements to leave
by train for St. Louis and thence by boat to New Orleans. He was scheduled to leave early Monday morning, May 22. Phil ached to see the men of his corps, at
that moment encamped at some distance from the capital. No, it could not be—orders were orders. Suddenly
his brooding thoughts were distracted by familiar
sounds—the hammering of horses hoofs, many hoofs,
coming closer, the steady tattoo punctuated occasionally by bugle notes.

Tumbling his battered meerschaum pipe into an ash-
tray, Phil hastened to one of the big curtained windows
of his room, opened it and stepped out onto the bal-

cony. He could see cavalry advancing toward the hotel down one of Washington's broad avenues, thousands of men, their silhouettes blurred by spring rain and mist. Soon its vanguard was near the hotel, heading for the area directly under the balcony. Phil's heart bounded. There could be no mistake—it was his cavalry, his boys.

The cavalry—Phil was totally unaware of it—had been ordered on that day to move to a camp closer to Washington, near Bladensburg, in preparation for the review. Knowing that Phil was at the hotel, his officers had decided to follow a very circuitous route which would bring them past the Willard Hotel. The men greeted these orders with cheers.

Overjoyed, Phil stood proudly on the balcony unofficially reviewing his men, grinning, alternating salutes with friendly waves of his hand.

In impressive array, the long files of mounted troopers with battle flags and guidons, wheels of the horse artillery and supply wagons rumbling on the pavement, trumpets sounding, moved past the hotel. Their uniforms were soaked by rain and splattered with mud, but the veterans of the Wilderness, the Shenandoah and Petersburg, gave Phil the "eyes right" with smart precision.

Phil watched the column until the last supply wagon had faded in the distance. The mighty little warrior brushed tears from his eyes as he re-entered the room— tears of deep pleasure at this unexpected demonstration of affection and respect from his fighting men.

The following day Phil left for New Orleans and

his new assignment. It can be said that the heroic phase of his life, the one which brought him greatest fame, ended with his departure from Washington. In the years ahead he would render outstanding service to his country but never again in the stirring role he played during the Civil War.

Behind the official announcements of Phil's new operation lay a deeper motive. During the Civil War, Napoleon III of France had engineered a coup in Mexico. French troops had been landed in that country; President Benito Juarez had been ousted and the Austrian Prince Maximilian and his wife Carlota were proclaimed Emperor and Empress of Mexico. During the Civil War the French puppet government had provided considerable help to the Confederates, including arms. Grant, now General-in-Chief, and the government wanted the Mexican republic restored.

The Government wished to avoid open armed intervention which might lead to war with France. Sheridan received secret instructions to help ex-President Juarez, still in northern Mexico, as much as possible. This included undercover shipment of arms to his followers. At the same time, Phil was to make as many threatening military gestures as possible along the border.

Phil carried out these instructions effectively. American bluff and pressure finally caused Napoleon to withdraw his troops in 1867, virtually abandoning the man he had placed on the "throne." Maximilian waged his own hopeless little war with some four thousand Mexican mercenaries against the swelling republican armies.

Mrs. Sheridan

His crumbling little army was wiped out, and Maximilian was captured and executed on June 19, 1867.

The government then ordered Sheridan to take command of the Department of the Missouri in which his main task would be to control or pacify Indians. In this post he became one of the four department commanders under General Sherman, commanding the Division of the Missouri.

In 1868, when Grant was elected president and Sherman appointed general-in-chief, Phil took over Sherman's position with the rank of Lieutenant General, headquarters Chicago.

In 1874 bachelor Phil, then in his early forties, received an arrow in his heart. At an army wedding, he met blonde, vivacious and comely Miss Irene Rucker, twenty-two-year-old daughter of General Daniel H. Rucker, quartermaster general of the Division of the Missouri. From that moment Phil courted her energetically and they were married on June 3, 1875. When their engagement first was made known, a Chicago newspaper announced it with the succinct headlines: "Great cavalry leader vanquished by blonde."

The marriage proved a very happy one and Irene bore him four children, Mary, the eldest, Irene and Louise, who were twins, and a boy, Philip Henry, Jr.

Phil was appointed army general-in-chief in 1883. The Sheridans moved to Washington and made their home at Rhode Island Avenue and 17th Street.

With the passage of the years, the lean cavalryman had become plump, making his appearance more comical than ever. He usually wore civilian clothes in Washington, and according to a New York *World* reporter was far from imposing in appearance.

"He wore upon the back of his round bullet head an old-fashioned silk hat, about two sizes too small, a short, light yellow-gray overcoat which had only two buttons and they were ready to fly off from the undue strain of Sheridan's round figure. The trousers were a gray plaid and fitted very snugly to the general's fat legs. His boots were thick soled and unblacked."

During his tenure as top commander, Phil also came to the parting of the roads with an old comrade in arms, George Crook. Phil criticized George's handling of a campaign against the Apaches. Crook was relieved of command at his own request but the episode completely soured their long-standing friendship. In the 1880's Phil was mentioned as a candidate for president, but he definitely opposed any moves to further such suggestions.

Early in the summer of 1887 the Sheridans rented a seaside cottage at Nonquit, Massachusetts, overlooking Martha's Vineyard and Nantucket. He liked the area so much that he ordered immediate construction of his own cottage in that area. But time was running out; his health was deteriorating.

In 1888 Phil suffered a series of heart attacks, which mounted in severity. On Sunday, August 5, 1888, ailing Phil, only fifty-seven years old, sat in an armchair in the new cottage near a large window overlooking the sea. Here a final attack overwhelmed him. That evening the "forked lightning" of the battlefield went on his last ride, despite skilled medical attention. As death came, he was administered the last rites of the Catholic Church while members of his family gathered weeping around his bedside.

The great warrior's body was transported to Washington for an impressive funeral service in St. Matthew's Catholic Church, attended by President and Mrs. Cleveland and a host of notables. A solemn requiem Mass was sung, with the Dominican Fathers of Somerset whom he had known in his youth among those present. Kneeling on their *prie-dieu* in front of the coffin were his widow and his brothers, Mike and John, and kneeling nearby the parents of his widow. His mother was too old at the time to make the long journey to Washington. His father had died in 1875.

In a moving sermon, Cardinal Gibbons praised the accomplishments and character of the Irish Catholic boy of Somerset who rose to dazzling fame.

"Comrades and companions of the illustrious dead, take hence your great leader," the cardinal said in conclusion. "Bear him to his last resting place, carry him gently, lovingly, and though you may not hope to attain his exalted rank you will strive at least to emulate him by the integrity of your private life, by your devotion to your country, and by upholding the honor of your military profession."

Through streets lined with silent thousands, the remains of "Little Phil" were borne away to the sound of muffled drums, and the coffin was lowered into its last resting place in Arlington National Cemetery.

Phil lies there today and his beloved black horse is not far away in the capitol. Rienzi died at a ripe old age in 1875, well cared for to the end. His body was embalmed and the famous horse, well preserved, is one of the striking exhibits in the Smithsonian Institution in Washington.

Phil still heads for Cedar Creek on Rienzi in magnificent but immobile defiance, his ride immortalized in a notable statue fashioned by Gutzon Borglum which today dominates Sheridan Circle in Washington, D. C.

FOR MORE ABOUT PHILIP SHERIDAN

Catton, Bruce. *This Hallowed Ground: The Story of the Union Side of the Civil War*. New York: Doubleday & Company, Inc., 1956.

Dupuy, R. Ernest and Dupuy, Trevor N. *The Compact History of the Civil War*. New York: Hawthorn Books, Inc., 1960.

Ned, G. Bradford (ed.). *Battles and Leaders of the Civil War*. Des Moines, Iowa: Meredith Press.

Reeder, Red. *Sheridan, the General Who Wasn't Afraid to Take a Chance*. Des Moines, Iowa: Meredith Press, 1962.

Stackpole, Edward J. *Sheridan in the Shenandoah*. Harrisburg, Pennsylvania: The Stackpole Company, 1961.

INDEX

Albany, New York, 13–14, 25
Aldrich's Station, Virginia, 123
Alger, Russell A., 61, 68–70, 72
Antietam, Maryland, 118
Apache Indians, 40, 181
Appomattox, Virginia, 164, 173
Arlington National Cemetery, 182
Atlanta, Georgia, 31, 139
Averill, W. W., 148

Baldwin, Mississippi, 64
Bates, Francis H., 44
Beauregard, P. G. T., 61, 64
Beaver Dam, Virginia, 124
Benicia Barracks, California, 44
Berryville, Virginia, 137–138, 140
Blair, Austin, 60–61
Booneville, Mississippi, 61–62, 64–65, 67–70, 72–73, 76, 79
battle of, 65, 72, 78
Booth, John Wilkes, 174
Borglum, Gutzon, 182
Boston, Massachusetts, 13
Bradfort Island, Washington, 52–54
Bragg, Braxton, 76–79, 87, 89–90, 96–97, 99–100, 104–105, 107–109, 112–114, 124
Buell, Don Carlos, 57, 77–82, 85
Buffalo, New York, 25
Bull Run, Virginia, battle of, 77
Burr, Frank, 16, 70
Butler, M. C., 128

Campbell, Archibald, 74–76
Card, James, 86

Carlota, Empress, 178
Cascade Indians, 54
Cassell, Sam, 16–18, 21
Cedar Creek, Virginia, 136, 149, 152–153, 155–157, 160, 162, 182
battle of, 164
Chalmers, James R., 68
Chaplin Heights, Kentucky, 81
Chaplin River, Kentucky, 79–80, 82
Charleston, West Virginia, 139
Chattanooga, Tennessee, 77, 93, 97, 99, 104–106, 115–116
battle of, 114
Chicago, Illinois, 179
Chickamauga Creek, Georgia, 97, 99–100
battle of, 99–100, 103, 105–108, 115
Chinook Indians, 54
"Churchbell Battery," 109, 114
Cincinnati, Ohio, 78
Clark, William, 21
Cleveland, Grover, 181
Cleveland, Ohio, 25
Cold Harbor, Virginia, 127–128, 134
Columbia River, Washington, 44, 48, 52–54
Comanche Indians, 36–37, 39–40
Compact History of the Civil War, 113, 168
Corinth, Mississippi, 61–62, 64, 70, 77, 85
Corpus Christi, Texas, 34, 37, 39
County Cavan, Ireland, 13

Crook, George, 26, 28, 44, 106, 134, 140–141, 143, 145–146, 149, 154–155, 167, 180–181
Cumberland, Army of the, 85, 98, 100, 102, 105–109, 112–114
Cumberland River, 97
Curtis, Samuel R., 58–60
Custer, George Armstrong, 120–121, 124–125, 128, 134, 153, 161–162, 167
Custer, Mrs. George A., 130

Dana, Charles, 107, 114
Danville, Virginia, 172
Davis, Jefferson, 172
Dinwiddie Courthouse, 167–169
Dupuy, R. Ernest, 113
Dupuy, Trevor N., 113

Early, Jubal A., 131–134, 136–142, 144–149, 152, 154–155, 162–164
Elliott, Washington, 61–62, 65
Emancipation Proclamation, 96
Emory, W. H., 155
Ewell, R. S., 172

Farmington, Mississippi, 62, 64
Fisher's Hill, Virginia, 142, 144–145, 149–150, 153, 163
Five Forks, Virginia, 170–172
Forsyth, James W., 118
Fort Clark, Texas, 37
Fort Duncan, Texas, 32–36, 39–42
Fort Reading, 42, 44–46
Fort Sumter, South Carolina, 55
Fort Vancouver, Washington, 48
Fort Yamhill, Oregon, 54–55
Frankfort, Kentucky, 79

Franklin, Kentucky, 31
Fredricksburg, Virginia, 121, 123
Fremont, John C., 58

Gaynor, Thomas, 13
Getty, George, 161
Gettysburg, battle of, 102, 167, 169, 171
Gilbert, C. C., 78
Gordon, James, 125
Gordon, John B., 154–155, 162
Grand Review of Union Soldiers, 176–177
Granger, Gordon, 60–62, 112, 114
Grant, Ulysses S., 57, 76–77, 87, 105–107, 109, 112, 114–115, 118, 121–122, 127–128, 130, 133–134, 136–137, 139–140, 142, 150–151, 164–167, 169, 172–173, 176, 179
Gregg, David McMurtrie, 120, 128
Griener, Henry, 10–11, 21
Greusel, Nicholas, 86

Halleck, Henry "Old Brains," 57–58, 60, 64, 73, 77, 115, 118, 151–152
Halltown, West Virginia, 136
Hampton, Wade, 128
Hardee, William, 90
Harpers Ferry, West Virginia, 132–134, 136, 139, 152
Haxall's Landing, Virginia, 122, 127
Haw's Shop, Virginia, 127
Herald, New York, 166
Hill, A. P., 168
Hinton, Richard, 16, 70
Hood, John Bell, 31

Hooker, Joseph, 106–107
Humphrey, Andrew, 168

Indianola, Texas, 33
Ireland, 13–14, 17

Jackson, James, 81
Jackson, Thomas "Stonewall," 133
Jefferson Barracks, Missouri, 55
Johnston, Albert Sidney, 57
Johnston, Joseph, 166, 171
Juarez, Benito, 178

Kernstown, Virginia, 164
Kershaw, James B., 136–137, 149, 154, 172
Knoxville, Tennessee, 77

La Pena, Camp, Texas, 36
La Pendencia, Texas, 36, 39
Laredo, Texas, 34
Lebanon, Missouri, 59
Lee, Curtis, 172
Lee, Fitzhugh, 128, 168
Lee, Robert E., 32, 78, 118, 121–125, 128, 136, 149, 163–168, 170–173
Lee, W. H. F., 128
Lincoln, Abraham, 57, 96, 117–118, 142, 163, 174
Lipan Indians, 36, 40
Little North Mountain, Virginia, 143–144, 146
Longstreet, James, 100, 102
Louisville, Kentucky, 78–79
Luray Valley, 144–145, 148
Lynchburg, Virginia, 172

Martinsburg, West Virginia, 139, 152

Massanutten Mountain, 143–145, 149, 153
Maximilian, Emperor, 178–179
McKinley, William, 160
McClellan, George, 118
McCook, Alexander, 82, 84–86, 90, 92
McLean, Eugene E., 35–36, 41
Meade, George Gordon, 119, 121–122, 127
Meigs, John R., 133
Merritt, Wesley, 134, 161–162, 167
Mexican War, 19
Middletown, Virginia, 149, 155, 161
Minor, Mary, 14
Missionary Ridge, Tennessee, 104–109, 115
battle of, 114
Mississippi, Army of, 58, 65, 73
Missouri, Department of the, 179
Missouri, Division of the, 179–180
Moore, T. W. C., 118
Morris, Thompson, 35–36
Mosby, John S., 134, 136, 174
Murfreesboro, Tennessee, 87–88, 96, 99

Napoleon III, 178
Nashville, Tennessee, 31, 85, 87, 93–94, 96–97
New Orleans, Louisiana, 33, 176–177
New World, 23, 25
Newport Barracks, Kentucky, 32
Newtown, Virginia, 160
Nez Perce Indians, 52
Nonquit, Massachusetts, 181

Northern Virginia, Army of, 118, 148, 173

Ohio, Army of the, 58, 77, 79, 85
Ohio in the War, 157
Opequon Creek, 138–139
  battle of, 144
Orchard Knob, Tennessee, 106–108, 112
Oregon territory, 44

Pea Ridge, Arkansas, 59
Perryville, Kentucky, 79, 81, 84, 98
  battle of, 84–85
Petersburg, Virginia, 150–152, 164–168, 171–172, 174–175, 177
Pickett, George, 168–171
Pit Indians, 44, 46, 48
Pittsburg Landing, Tennessee, 60–61
Pleasanton, Alfred, 119
Potomac, Army of the, 106, 116, 118–120, 122, 128, 131, 134, 165, 167
Price, Sterling, 57–58

Rains, Gabriel, 48–49, 51–52, 127
Read, James Buchanan, 142
Reid, Whitelaw, 157
Richmond, Virginia, 77, 121–125, 127–130, 134, 136–137, 150–152, 164–166, 168, 171–172
Rienzi, 55, 75, 79, 81–82, 90, 93, 98, 102, 108–109, 112, 116–117, 120, 123, 131–132, 138, 142, 147, 152, 156, 162, 167, 182
Rienzi, Mississippi, 69, 73–74, 78
Ritchie, Thomas, 20

Rolla, Missouri, 58–59
Rome, Georgia, 76–77
Rosecrans, William S., 73, 85, 87, 89–90, 92–94, 96, 99–100, 103, 105–106
Rossville, Georgia, 102
Rucker, Daniel H., 180
Rucker, Irene, *see also* Sheridan, Mrs. Irene, 179–180

San Francisco, California, 44
Schofield, John M., 31
Shenandoah Valley, Virginia, 130, 132–134, 139, 152, 163, 166, 174, 177
  Army of the, 138–139, 150–151, 156, 164, 167
Sheridan, Mrs. Irene, 180–182
Sheridan, Irene (Phil's daughter), 180
Sheridan, John (Phil's father), 13, 20–21, 182
Sheridan, John (Phil's brother), 14, 181
Sheridan, Louise, 180
Sheridan, Mary (Phil's mother), 13–14, 17, 21, 182
Sheridan, Mary (Phil's sister), 14
Sheridan, Mary (Phil's daughter), 180
Sheridan, Michael, 14, 118, 150, 181
Sheridan, Patrick H., 14
Sheridan, Philip Henry, Jr., 180
Sheridan, Rosa, 14
Sherman, William Tecumseh, 55, 57, 60, 106–107, 139, 166, 179
Shiloh Meeting House, Tennessee, battle of, 60, 77
Sill, Joshua, 31, 86, 90–91

Slocum, Henry, 26–28, 106
Smith, E. Kirby, 77–79, 176
Smith, Persifer F., 34
Smithsonian Institution, 182
Somerset, Ohio, 9, 13–14, 16–18, 21, 25–26, 28, 32–33, 55, 73, 115, 121, 181–182
Southwest, Army of the, 58
Spokane Indians, 52
Spotsylvania Courthouse, Virginia, 123
battle of, 121
Springfield, Missouri, 59
St. Louis, Missouri, 55, 57–58, 60, 176
Stanley, David, 23–25
Stanton, Edwin, 118, 150–152, 174
Staunton, Virginia, 164
Stones River, Tennessee, 89, 98, 100
battle of, 31, 96
Strasburg, Virginia, 136, 141–142, 144–145, 149, 154
Stuart, J. E. B., 121–125, 127–128

Talbot, John, 19
Tennessee, Confederate Army of the, 57
Tennessee, Union Army of the, 31, 57, 106
Terrill, William R., 28, 30, 80–81
Texas, Department of, 34
Thomas, George, 32, 86, 100, 102–103, 106–107, 112, 114, 116
Todd's Tavern, Virginia, 121
Torbert, Alfred T. A., 120, 134, 148
Trans-Mississippi, Army of the, 176

Trevilian, Virginia, 128, 130
Tupelo, Mississippi, 64, 77

Umatilla Indians, 52

Van Buren, E. M., 37, 39
Vicksburg, Mississippi, battle of, 102, 106

Walker, J. G., 40
Walla Walla Indians, 52
Warren, Gouverneur, 167–171
Washington, D.C., 115, 117–118, 132, 134, 142, 150–153, 163, 174–178, 180, 182
Waynesboro, Virginia, 164
West Point Military Academy, 15, 20–21, 23–28, 30–33, 35, 80, 85–86, 89, 106
White House Landing, Virginia, 129, 164
Wilderness, battle of the, 121
Williamson, R. S., 44–48
Wilson, James H., 120, 141
Winchester, Virginia, 137–142, 149, 151–153, 155–157
Third Battle of, 139
Wright, Horatio, 138, 146–147, 150, 154–155

Yakima Indian War, 48–52
Yakima Indians, 48–49, 51–52, 54
Yellow Tavern, Virginia, 124
battle of, 125
Young, H. K., 137
Young, Father Dominic, 20–21, 181
Young, Father Joshua, 20–21, 181

Zanesville, Ohio, 21–22, 25

THE AUTHOR AND HIS BOOK

ALBERT ORBAAN *was born in Rome, Italy. His father was from Holland and his mother from America. He went to high school in Switzerland and also attended college there at the University of Neuchâtel. After becoming a United States citizen, Mr. Orbaan served in the U.S. Army Military Intelligence division during World War II and was stationed in Luxembourg and France. Although he lives in New York City and has his studio there, Mr. Orbaan is an enthusiast of outdoor sports, including tennis, skiing, skating, and swimming. He has previously written and illustrated* Powder and Steel *(John Day Co., 1963) and* With Banners Flying *(John Day Co., 1960). For this book, Mr. Orbaan has supplemented his text with numerous diagrams of military compaigns.*

FORKED LIGHTNING *(Hawthorn, 1964) was designed by Stefan Salter and completely manufactured by American Book–Stratford Press. The body type is Linotype Janson, based on the letters of Anton Janson, a Dutch punchcutter who worked between 1660 and 1687.*

A HAWTHORN BOOK

Published with ecclesiastical approbation.

ABOUT CREDO BOOKS

CREDO BOOKS is an important new series of biographies that will appeal to both boys and girls. The subjects of these biographies are Catholics, but their stories are not of their faith so much as how that faith helped them to lead remarkable lives. Past and present will be represented here: a sculptor who left a priceless treasure of art to mankind, or a movie star who was an idol to young and old alike; the president of a South American country who fought against and lost his life to Communist terrorists. Heroes are made by the greatness of the human spirit and all the figures to be portrayed in CREDO BOOKS were great in spirit, courage and effort, no matter what task they took upon themselves.

The authors of these new books have been carefully chosen both for their ability to make biography come alive for young people and their knowledge of their subjects. Such authors as Terry Morris, Albert Orbaan, Donald Demarest, Gary Webster, Ruth Hume, Frank Kolars and Jack Steffan will be represented.

To give CREDO BOOKS the benefit of their knowledge and experience, an editorial board of distinguished representatives from the fields of education, librarianship and the Catholic Press, as well as Hawthorn's own editorial staff, choose both subject and author for each book in the series.

As an example of the variety of personalities in this new series, you will find the following figures portrayed.

Operation Escape: The Adventure of Father O'Flaherty, by Daniel Madden

To Far Places: The Story of Francis X. Ford, by Eva K. Betz

The Lion of Poland: The Story of Paderewski, by Ruth and Paul Hume

The Conscience of a King: The Story of Thomas More, by Margaret Stanley-Wrench

Pen and Bayonet: The Story of Joyce Kilmer, by Norah Smaridge

The Man Who Found Out Why: The Story of Gregor Mendel, by Gary Webster

The Tall American: The Story of Gary Cooper, by Richard Gehman

Wings of an Eagle: The Story of Michelangelo, by Anne M. Peck with Frank and Dorothy Getlein

The Door of Hope: The Story of Katharine Drexel, by Katherine Burton

Fire of Freedom: The Story of Col. Carlos Castillo Armas, by Jack Steffan

Doctor America: The Story of Tom Dooley, by Terry Morris

The Sea Tiger: The Story of Pedro Menéndez, by Frank Kolars

The First Californian: The Story of Fray Junípero Serra, by Donald Demarest

Wilderness Explorer: The Story of Samuel de Champlain, by Charles Morrow Wilson